# Geology of the Kintail district

This memoir describes the geology of a sparsely populated area in the Northern Highlands having a rugged, mountainous topography that includes several peaks and ridges rising more than 1000 m above OD. The area lies within the Caledonian orogenic belt and is formed chiefly of metamorphosed sediments (Moine) with several extensive, and numerous minor, occurrences of Lewisian rocks which represent fragments of the basement upon which the Moine sediments were deposited. The large area of Lewisian rocks north of Loch Duich extends westwards into the Glenelg district (Sheet 71E) where it lies close to the Moine Thrust, the most easterly of the thrusts separating the Caledonian orogenic belt from its foreland. Numerous thin, discontinuous inliers of Lewisian rock occur interbanded with the Moine to the east of the Glenelg inlier; they have probably reached their present position during movement along slides (ductile thrusts), although some may lie in the cores of early isoclinal folds. A previously unrecognised rock type, termed quartz-biotite rock, does not appear to be a part of the Moine succession or the Lewisian basement. It is confined to slide zones and may be a restite resulting from the partial melting of Moine psammite during sliding.

The Lewisian north of Loch Duich and in the Glenelg area (Sheet 71E) consists of contrasting western and eastern facies separated from each other by a zone of extreme deformation. The former, composed of migmatite and granodioritic acid gneiss, together with the remnants of basic intrusions, has been affected by granulite facies metamorphism and was later cut by basic dykes which may be the equivalents of the Scourie dykes in the Lewisian of the Caledonian foreland. The eastern facies is also partly composed of migmatitic gneiss but contains, in addition, metasedimentary rocks and there is isotopic evidence indicating that it was subjected to eclogite facies metamorphism of Grenville age.

The Moine rocks were originally deposited as sandstones, siltstones and mudstones in a shelf environment. They, and the underlying Lewisian rocks, were metamorphosed and intensely deformed during t orogeny. Further south the into three informal lithostratigraphic divisions, the lower two (Morar and Glenfinnan divisions) being separated by a major tectonic dislocation, the Sgurr Beag Slide. The complexity of the folding and lack of distinctive marker horizons has so far prevented the establishment of a regional stratigraphy within the two divisions. Nevertheless both of the lower two divisions, and the Sgurr Beag Slide, have been recognised in the Kintail district, and a succession of local significance is proposed for the Morar division.

Meta-igneous rocks make up a substantial proportion of the Lewisian outcrop, and a number of minor basic bodies, now represented by hornblende schists, were intruded into the Moine rocks before the Caledonian orogeny. Late Caledonian igneous activity continued into early Devonian times with the intrusion of the gabbro to monzonite Ratagain Plutonic Complex and a variety of minor intrusions. Renewed activity during the late Carboniferous and Permian produced east–west-trending camptonite-monchiquite dykes, which are particularly common in the north of the district. The very few Tertiary dolerite dykes, probably emanating from the Skye volcanic centre, represent the final igneous episode.

Numerous faults occur throughout the area and the northeast-trending Strathconon Fault has been shown to have a net sinistral displacement of 6 kms.

The pre-Quaternary land surface was modified by glaciations throughout the Pleistocene. Following the Devensian glaciation the main valleys were reoccupied by glaciers during the Loch Lomond Stadial, at about 11 000 to 10 000 BP, and when the ice finally retreated the valley floors remained mantled with till, hummocky moraine and fluvioglacial sands and gravels.

*Frontispiece*   Glen Shiel, with moraine hummocks and rock-cored mounds in the middle ground and Moine psammite forming the mountains of The Saddle and Spidean Dhomhuill Bhic in the background. (D2799)

BRITISH GEOLOGICAL SURVEY

F MAY
J D PEACOCK
D I SMITH and
A J BARBER

# Geology of the Kintail district

Memoir for 1:50 000 sheet 72W and part of 71E
(Scotland)

CONTRIBUTORS

G C Clark

*Ratagain Complex*
D H W Hutton
W E Stephens
B Yardley
M McErlean
A N Halliday

LONDON: HMSO   1993

iv

ISBN 0 11 884484 9

*Bibliographical reference*

MAY, F, PEACOCK, J D, SMITH, D I, and BARBER, A J. 1993. Geology of the Kintail district. *Memoir of the British Geological Survey*, Sheet 72W and part of 71E (Scotland).

*Authors*

F May
J D Peacock
D I Smith
*British Geological Survey, Edinburgh*
A J Barber
*Royal Holloway and Bedford New College*

*Contributors*

G C Clark
*British Geological Survey, Edinburgh*
D H W Hutton
*University of Durham*
W E Stephens
*University of St Andrews*
B Yardley
*University of Leeds*
M McErlean
*University of Durham*
A N Halliday
*Scottish Universities Research and Reactor Centre*

*Other publications of the Survey dealing with this and adjoining districts*

**BOOKS**

*British Regional Geology*
The Northern Highlands (4th edition) 1989
*Memoirs*
The geology of Glenelg, Lochalsh and south east part of Skye, 1910
The geology of central Ross-shire, 1913
The geology of the Glen Affric district, 1992
*Technical Report*
The Ratagain Plutonic Complex, WA/90/79

**MAPS**

*1:625 000*
United Kingdom (North Sheet)
Solid Geology 1979
Quaternary Geology 1977
Bouguer Anomaly 1981
Aeromagnetic Anomaly 1972

*1:250 000*
Great Glen Sheet (57°N 06°W)
Solid Geology, 1989

*1:63 360*
Sheet 71    Broadford, 1896
Sheet 81    Raasay 1896
Sheet 82    Lochcarron 1913

*1:50 000*
Sheet 62W (Loch Quoich) Solid and Drift editions 1975
Sheet 71E (Lochalsh) Solid and Drift editions 1976
Sheet 72E (Glen Affric) Solid and Drift editions 1986
Sheet 81E (Loch Torridon) Solid and Drift editions 1975

Printed in the UK for HMSO
Dd 291143 C8 4/93 531 12521

# CONTENTS

FIGURES

TABLES

PLATES

# PREFACE

This memoir describes the geology of a rugged mountainous region on the western seaboard of the north-west Highlands of Scotland. It is a sparsely populated area used for sporting activities (deer stalking, fishing) as well as forestry and the farming of fish and hill sheep. It attracts many visitors wishing to enjoy the natural scenic beauty and to pursue outdoor activities such as hill walking, rambling and sailing. The region is of geological significance because it lies near the western margin of the Caledonian orogenic belt, just a few kilometres east of the thrust zone separating the orogen from the foreland. The Kintail area is largely made up of deformed and metamorphosed Precambrian shelf sediments (the Moine) and the underlying basement rocks (the Lewisian) upon which they were deposited. The occurrence of a large area of Lewisian rocks, as well as numerous other small inliers interbanded with Moine metasediments, is of particular interest. The memoir provides a descriptive account of the complex basement/cover relationships to be seen. The Sgurr Beag Slide, a structural break of regional significance within the Moine rocks, and which has been traced for many tens of kilometres, was first recognised in the area described by this memoir. The region is crossed by a large number of sheets and dykes of various compositions and ages but there is only one major igneous intrusion, the Ratagain Plutonic Complex, which ranges in composition from gabbro to monzonite. Some of the phases have remarkably high contents of some trace elements, notably Sr, Ba (and the light rare-earth elements), resulting in what appears to be unusual primary magmatic occurrences of baryte ($BaSO_4$) and celestine ($SrSO_4$).

The effects of the Quaternary Ice Age have strongly influenced the present land surface. Glaciation and deglaciation shaped the landscape to its present form and interpretation of the geomorphology, as well as of the glacial and postglacial deposits laid down when the ice finally retreated, has contributed significantly to our fuller understanding of Quaternary geology.

The survey of the Kintail District has shown that there are large reserves of hard-rock aggregate among the solid rocks, and very limited sand and gravel resources among the Quaternary glacial deposits. Small indications of base and precious metals have been recorded in narrow veins associated with faulting in various places, but there is no evidence to indicate the presence of potentially economic metalliferous mineral deposits. Undoubtedly the most valuable natural resource of the area is the, as yet, unspoilt mountain scenery and it is to be hoped that a better understanding of the underlying geology may help towards a fuller appreciation of this national asset and its careful conservation.

P J Cook, DSc
*Director*

*British Geological Survey*
*Keyworth*
*Nottingham NG12 5GG*

October 1992

ONE

# Introduction

Sheet 72W, Kintail, covers an area of rugged high relief with several peaks and ridges rising to over 1000 m above OD. In the west are the sea lochs, Loch Hourn, Loch Duich and Loch Long, and trending approximately north–south through the area is the principal watershed of the northern Highlands (Figure 1). Climatically the area has a very high annual rainfall, and records maintained by the North of Scotland Hydroelectric Board indicate the annual average to be not less than 3.0 m on the high ground of the watershed and not less than 2.0 m at sea level.

Large-scale glacial sculpturing has considerably modified the preglacial landscape and the principal valleys have been enlarged and deepened. The main watershed is transected by several prominent glacial breaches trending approximately east–west and which provide access routes across the area. Rough tracks link Glen Elchaig to Loch Monar, Glen Lichd to Glen Affric and the breach linking Glen Shiel to Glen Moriston contains the main A87 trunk road (Figure 1). Corries are well developed on the northern and eastern slopes of many of the higher hills and the three sea lochs mentioned above occupy over-deepened ice basins.

The area is sparsely populated and most of the inhabitants are concentrated along the shores of Loch Duich, at Inverinate (pop. 154, 1971 census) and Shiel Bridge (pop. less than 100, 1971 census). These population figures increase significantly with the influx of holiday visitors during the summer months and the main occupational activities of the resident population are connected to tourism or employment on the large agricultural, sporting estates of the area.

Geological surveying commenced at the end of the last century, the work being part of the primary survey of Glenelg, Lochalsh and southeast part of Skye (Clough, 1901; Peach et al., 1910). On Sheet 72W the work was confined to ground adjacent to Loch Duich and ceased in 1911. Although studies were carried out on rocks from near Loch Duich (Tilley, 1936; Alderman, 1936) there was no further reported geological mapping until after 1950 when univer-

sity research was undertaken in selected areas (Clifford, 1957; Ramsay, 1957; Dhonau, 1960; Sutton and Watson, 1958) and the primary survey of the sheet recommenced in 1963. University research continued (Barber, 1968; Simony, 1963, 1973; Tanner 1971; Tanner et al., 1970; Fleuty, 1974; Rathbone and Harris, 1979; Langford, 1980) and some of the results of the primary survey were included in a review of Moine stratigraphy by Johnstone et al. (1969). Aspects of the minor intrusions have been studied by Smith (1979) and the Ratagain Plutonic Complex by Nicholls (1951a, b), Dhonau (1964), Stephens (1981), and Hutton et al. (1990). The Quaternary history has been discussed by Peacock (1975) and in its regional context by Sissons (1976, 1983).

The geological survey of Sheet 72W was undertaken by a large number of BGS geologists between 1963 and 1975 — N G Berridge, G C Clark, D J Fettes, A L Harris, W G Henderson, F May, J D Peacock, D I Smith, T E Smith and R A Waters. In addition the memoir includes information from university research studies by A J Barber (1956–59), M J Fleuty (1970–72), P S Simony (1961–63), and P W G Tanner (1963–65).

While mapping was in progress several of the original surveyors left the project and the assembling of a coherent account of the complex geology, based upon the mapping of so many geologists over a long period of time, has proved a difficult task and the account which follows represents the collation of many fragments of data and interpretations; some aspects of the geology, notably the account of the metamorphic history, are incomplete. Since the survey was completed further university research has been undertaken over the Ratagain Plutonic Complex. The results of this work, which extended into part of sheet 71E, have been summarised by D H W Hutton and his co-workers and are included in this account.

The memoir has been compiled by Dr May and Dr Peacock.

**Figure 1**
Physiographic
and locality map
of the Kintail
District.

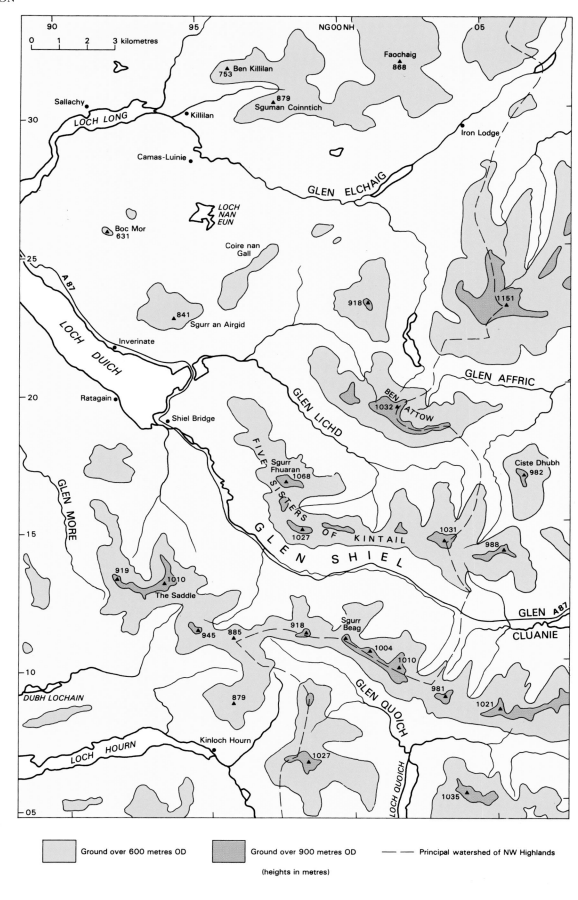

0  1  2  3 kilometres

NG 00 NH

Ben Killilan
▲ 753

Faochaig
▲ 868

Sallachy •

LOCH LONG

Killilan •

▲ 879
Sguman Coinntich

Iron Lodge •

Camas-Luinie •

GLEN ELCHAIG

30

LOCH
NAN
EUN

Boc Mor
⊙ 631

Coire nan
Gall

25

918 ▲

▲ 1151

A 87

841
▲

Sgurr an Airgid

LOCH DUICH

Inverinate •

GLEN AFFRIC

BEN ATTOW
1032 ▲

20

Ratagain •

GLEN LICHD

Ciste Dhubh
▲ 982

Shiel Bridge •

FIVE SISTERS OF KINTAIL

Sgurr
Fhuaran
▲ 1068

GLEN MORE

1031
▲

988 ▲

▲ 1027

15

GLEN SHIEL

919
▲ 1010
The Saddle

GLEN A 87

945 ▲   885 ▲     918 ▲   Sgurr
                          Beag
                          ▲ 1004

CLUANIE

10

879 ▲

1010 ▲

DUBH LOCHAIN

981 ▲

GLEN QUOICH

1021 ▲

LOCH HOURN

Kinloch Hourn •

1027 ▲

LOCH QUOICH

05

1035 ▲

☐ Ground over 600 metres OD          ■ Ground over 900 metres OD          - - - Principal watershed of NW Highlands

(heights in metres)

TWO

# Regional setting and summary of geology

The Kintail district lies within the Caledonian orogenic belt and is formed chiefly of Moine metamorphosed sedimentary rocks (Figure 2). Within the district there are several major and numerous minor occurrences of gneisses correlated with the Lewisian of the Caledonian Foreland and which are considered to represent fragments of the basement upon which the Moine rocks were deposited. Both the Lewisian and Moine of the Kintail district are part of the Moine nappe and rest on the Moine Thrust, the most easterly of the thrusts separating the orogenic belt from the Foreland (Figure 2). The Moine and Lewisian rocks are cut by several suites of minor intrusions and by the Ratagain Plutonic Complex.

The Lewisian rocks form large outcrops in the extreme north-west, where they are part of the extensive Glenelg–Attadale inlier overlying the Moine Thrust. Lewisian rocks also occur as thin discontinuous enclaves elsewhere within the Moine succession. The Lewisian of the Glenelg–Attadale inlier has been divided into a western facies formed mainly of migmatitic and granodioritic acid gneisses with amphibolite masses, and an eastern facies of migmatitic gneisses (blastomylonitic in part) with meta-igneous rocks represented by amphibolite, eclogite and pyroxenite, and undoubted metasedimentary rocks such as forsterite marble, eulysite and garnet-biotite gneiss. The enclaves of Lewisian within the Moine succession are similarly of variable rock type, mainly hornblende gneiss, but also including marbles, and serpentinites. These enclaves have been interpreted either as the cores of early isoclinal folds of the Lewisian basement or as tectonically emplaced slices located along slide zones (ductile thrusts).

The Moine rocks were originally laid down as sediments upon metamorphosed and deformed Lewisian basement, but the original unconformable contact has been obscured by later structural events so that the bedding in the Moine is subparallel to the layered structure of the Lewisian. The subsequent metamorphism has converted the sandstones to a quartzofeldspathic rock (psammite), the shales to mica schist (pelite) and the sandy shales or shaly sandstones to quartz-mica schist (semipelite). Calcareous lenses, which probably originated as concretions, are now represented by narrow bands of calcsilicate rock and form a minor constituent of the total Moine succession. Included in the Moine are rare bands or lenses of hornblende rock, locally very garnet-iferous, which represent metamorphosed minor intrusions.

The Moine rocks of the Scottish Highlands north of the Great Glen have been divided into three broad tectono-stratigraphic units, termed the Morar, Glenfinnan and Loch Eil divisions (Johnstone et al., 1969). The Moine rocks in the Kintail district have been grouped into the Morar and Glenfinnan divisions because of their continuity of outcrop and overall lithological similarity with the rocks of the type areas. Representatives of the Loch Eil Division are absent in Sheet 72W (Figure 1).

The Morar Division, made up dominantly of psammitic rocks, overlies the Lewisian of the Glenelg–Attadale inlier and contains numerous tectonically emplaced slices of Lewisian. South of Loch Hourn local stratigraphic successions have been established (Richey and Kennedy, 1939; Ramsay and Spring, 1962) but attempts to extend these successions on a regional scale have met with limited success and in the central part of the Kintail district a lithostratigraphic succession within the Morar Division has not been established. A local succession within the Morar Division north of the Strathconon Fault is described in this report and it has similarities with the successions established south of Loch Hourn.

The Glenfinnan Division has a varied lithology, consisting of thick bands of pelite, semipelite and psammite as well as thinly banded (striped) rocks consisting of psammite and pelite. The varied lithology and the striped rock units are distinctive features of the Glenfinnan Division.

The rocks of the Morar Division are separated from the Glenfinnan Division by the Sgurr Beag Slide which is considered to be a tectonic dislocation of regional significance. The age relationship between the divisions is therefore uncertain. Johnstone et al. (1969) suggested that the Morar Division was older, although locally and north of Sheet 72W, in central Ross-shire, rocks of the Glenfinnan Division also directly overlie Lewisian (Tanner et al., 1970). The Sgurr Beag Slide has been traced across the Kintail district from Loch Hourn in the south to Glen Elchaig in the north, a distance of some 25 kms. A slide zone separated from the main trace of the Sgurr Beag Slide by post-Caledonian faulting and containing Lewisian slices occurs at Coire nan Gall and has been interpreted as the Sgurr Beag Slide. Simony (1973) suggested a slide zone in the Shiel Bridge area, south of the Strathconon Fault, to be a further extension of the Sgurr Beag Slide.

Radiometric dates obtained from Moine rocks outside the area indicate they were deformed and metamorphosed at about 450 Ma, during the Caledonian orogeny, and were probably affected, in part at least, by earlier Precambrian episodes of folding and metamorphism at about 750 Ma and 1000 Ma.

Igneous intrusions emplaced in the Lewisian and Moine rocks have a wide range of age and composition. The earliest representatives were intensely metamorphosed and deformed during the Precambrian history of the Lewisian. Transgressive granitic pegmatite veins are common in most parts of the Moine and locally are sufficiently abundant to form a ramifying network within the metamorphic rocks. Some of these veins are probably of pre-Caledonian age. Late Caledonian intrusions include suites that were emplaced before tectonic movement had ceased and include minor intrusions of felsic porphyrite, microdiorite and appinite, some of which show an internal foliation. The

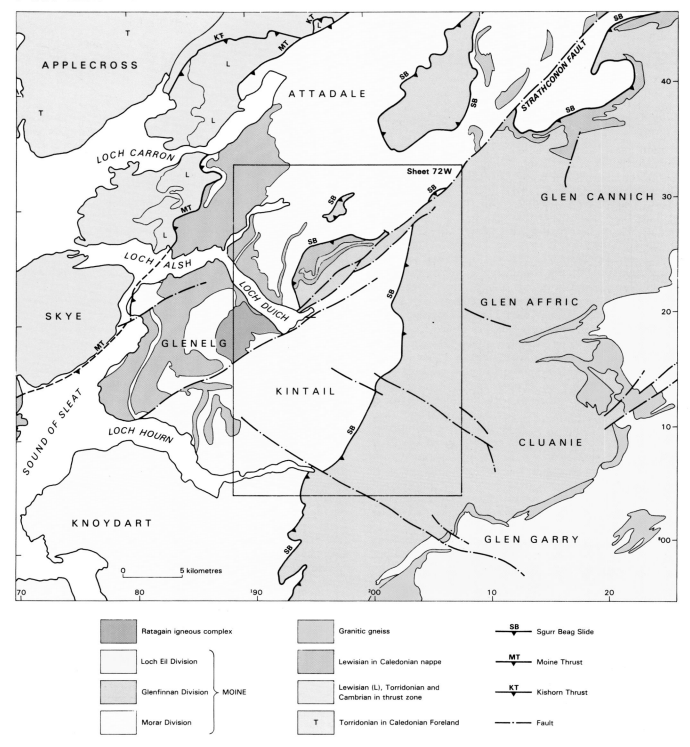

**Figure 2** Regional geological setting of the Kintail District.

Ratagain Complex was emplaced in postorogenic times and is probably of Mid-Silurian age. The intrusion is exceptional in having anomalous high Ba and Sr elemental values (Stephens et al., 1981, Hutton et al., 1990). Minor intrusions that are spatially related to the complex include porphyrite and microdiorite, and there are more widely distributed NW-and WNW-trending lamprophyre and felsite dykes. Dykes of the Permo-Carboniferous camptonite–monchiquite suite are abundant to the north of the Strathconon Fault. The final igneous episode is represented by a few dolerite dykes, of possible Tertiary age, restricted to the west of the area. Small bodies of metasomite, forming irregularly shaped discordant masses, have been located near Loch Hourn and in Glen Elchaig; they are cut by late-tectonic microdiorite and felsic porphyrite dykes and metasomatism probably took place after the main regional metamorphism.

The major faults in the area trend between NE and SE. The most obvious is the NE-trending Strathconon Fault which has a vertical downthrow to the south and a net sinistral displacement of approximately 6 km. Several discrete faults have been mapped and the Strathconon Fault is a zone of faulting some 1–2 km wide. The Kinlochhourn Fault trends SE and has a net dextral displacement of approximately 1 km.

The effects of the Quaternary glaciation upon the land surface are profound. Many of the landforms and deposits probably date from the Late Devensian glaciation some 18 000 BP. At the maximum of this glaciation ice movement was from east to west with the iceshed near to the east margin of the sheet. Even the highest mountains show evidence of ice action with 'whalebacks' and frost-shattered surfaces extending almost to the summits. The main valleys were re-occupied by glaciers during the Loch Lomond Readvance, between 11 000 BP and 10 000 BP. The limits of the Loch Lomond Readvance glaciers extend beyond the margins of the sheet and most of the glacial deposits in the district are attributed to this later glacial activity.

For the following account the metamorphic rocks of the Kintail district have been divided into six geographical areas of unequal size (Figure 3). Area 1 is underlain by the Lewisian Glenelg inlier; Areas 2 and 3 occur east of the Glenelg inlier and north of the Strathconon Fault and are made up chiefly of Moine rocks but with numerous inliers of Lewisian. Area 4 includes a varied assemblage of Moine rocks with thin intercalations of Lewisian located south of the Strathconon Fault; Area 5 is underlain by rocks of the Morar Division lying west of the Sgurr Beag Slide and east of Area 4. Area 6 consists of a wide outcrop of rocks of the Glenfinnan Division located east of the Sgurr Beag Slide. The deformation events recognised in the Lewisian and Moine rocks vary from place to place in the six areas and there are still

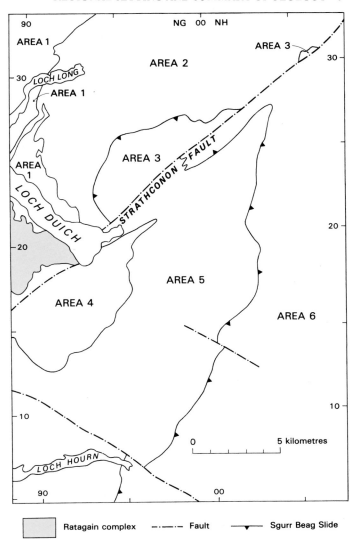

**Figure 3** Location of sub-areas used for the description of Lewisian and Moine rocks.

uncertainties over the correlation of the effects of some of the events across Kintail. Consequently, in the account which follows the deformation events are restricted to the major units in which they are recognised by use of subscript L for Lewisian and M for Moine. The intrusive rocks are described in terms of pre-Caledonian, Caledonian and post-Caledonian igneous events. A brief description of the whole of the Ratagain Plutonic Complex which extends on to Sheet 71E is included. The final chapters describe faulting, mineralisation and the Pleistocene and Recent events.

6

## THREE

# Lewisian

## INTRODUCTION

In the Northern Highlands the close similarity of certain out-crops of rock lying east of the Moine Thrust and rocks form-ing the Lewisian complex of the Caledonian Foreland has long been recognised and the early surveyors regarded the former outcrops as inliers of Lewisian Gneiss which original-ly made up the basement upon which the Moine sedimentary succession was deposited. Subsequent work has amply con-firmed that these inliers contain rocks which record pre-Moine igneous and metamorphic events although the simple anticlinal structures with Lewisian cores, postulated by the early workers, have been found inadequate to account for the presence of all the outcrops of Lewisian found amongst the Moine. It is now generally accepted that sliding (ductile thrusting) as well as isoclinal folding has controlled the emplacement of the basement slices.

The greatest diversity of rock type is encountered in the Glenelg inlier, north of Loch Duich, where evidence for the complex pre-Moine metamorphic and igneous history is still preserved. East of the Glenelg inlier occur many small, nar-row enclaves of distinctive rock types, some less than 1 m wide, within the Moine succession which have been cor-related with the Lewisian. The correlation in many examples is based primarily on similarity of rock type, since intense Caledonian deformation and metamorphism has destroyed all evidence of a pre-Moine history. Hornblende schists and gneisses are common rock types to be found in these enclaves, but serpentinites and marbles, rocks quite distinc-tive from the adjacent Moine succession, also occur.

## LEWISIAN OF AREA 1

The rocks around Loch Duich and Loch Long form part of the largest outcrop of basement gneisses, the Glenelg–Attadale Lewisian inlier, within the Caledonian orogenic belt of the Northern Highlands. The inlier is elongated in a north–south direction, extending for a distance of 30 km from Loch Carron to Loch Hourn and was originally mapped by Peach, Horne, Hinxman and Clough (Peach et al., 1907, 1910, 1913, Clough, 1901). Later studies of parts of the inlier have been carried out by Ramsay (1957, 1960), Sutton and Watson (1958), Sanders (1972), Sanders et al. (1984), and Barber and May (1975). There is also a useful excursion guide which includes the Loch Duich area (Barber et al., 1978). The ground north of Sallachy was mapped by one of the authors (FM) but the account of the ground to the south is almost entirely based on the published and un-published work of A J Barber (1968) with some additional information from an unpublished thesis by Sanders (1972).

In the Kintail area the rock units dip generally eastwards and at the western margin of the inlier (on Sheet 71E) the Lewisian rests on a thin band of Moine psammite separating the inlier from the Moine Thrust. Within the inlier the Lewi-sian rocks are divided into two parts by a zone of strongly deformed rocks which includes a schist derived partly from Lewisian gneisses and partly from Moine semipelite, as well as psammite of typical Moine aspect. The outcrops on either side of this strip show distinct characteristics and are termed the Western and Eastern Lewisian (Figure 4). The Western Lewisian consists of migmatitic and granodioritic acid gneisses, basic rocks such as pyroxene-hornblende-granulite, amphibolite, hornblende-schist and rare ultrabasic rocks. Many original Lewisian textures and structures are preserved in this part of the inlier. The Eastern Lewisian contains a great variety of rock types, including some of undoubted sedimentary origin such as forsterite-marble and garnet-biotite-gneiss as well as hornblende- and biotite-gneiss and eclogite derived from igneous rocks. This part of the inlier was strongly deformed after the deposition of the Moine and the presence of much blastomylonite is a notable feature. On the eastern side of the inlier the Lewisian passes beneath the main outcrop of the Moine. Towards Loch Long the strongly deformed zone separating the two parts of the inlier approaches the main Moine outcrop and continues northwards as the Basal Semipelite of the Moine.

### Western Lewisian

The rock units making up the western Lewisian have a len-ticular form and dip in a general way towards the ESE. The most abundant rock types are acid to intermediate gneisses which can be subdivided into migmatitic gneiss and grano-dioritic gneiss although these are not shown separately on the 1:50 000 map.

#### MIGMATITIC GNEISS

The migmatitic gneiss is a coarse-grained pale-coloured rock made up of oligoclase, quartz, hornblende and/or biotite with bands, pods and irregular clots of basic material. The banding is commonly lenticular in form and flow folded. In-dividual bands are usually only a few centimetres thick and traceable for less than a metre. The basic portion of the migmatite is composed either of coarse speckled amphibo-lite, identical to the larger basic masses represented on the map, or of coarse hornblendite. Contacts between amphibo-lite and the enclosing acid gneiss tend to be hazy and diffuse, while the hornblendite pods have sharp contacts, often margined by a thin zone of biotite flakes aligned parallel to the margin of the pod. A notable feature of the migmatitic gneiss is the presence, at a few localities, of large por-phyroblastic hornblende crystals up to 90 mm in length which commonly cut across the banding. The greatest development of the porphyroblasts is in the marginal parts of the inlier at Avernish and Maol Beag (Sheet 71E) and at Attadale (Sheet 82).

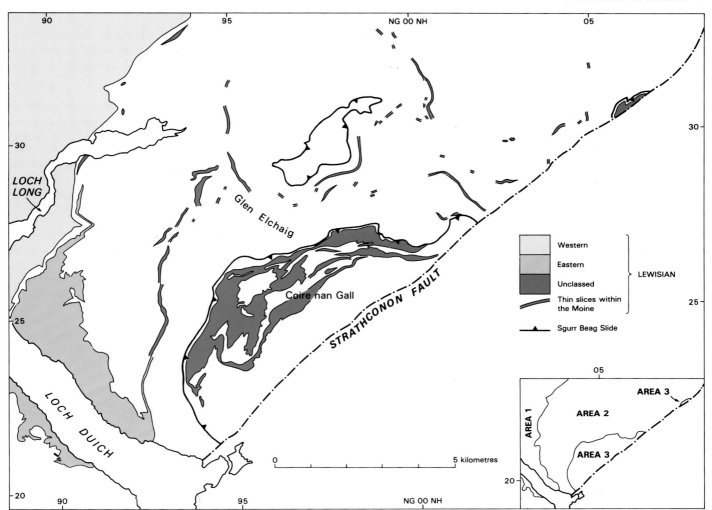

**Figure 4**   Distribution of Lewisian rocks north of the Strathconon Fault.

Blastomylonitic derivatives of migmatitic gneiss occur along narrow zones within the inlier. They have a platy fabric and contain lens-shaped relics of feldspar in a fine-grained matrix.

GRANODIORITIC GNEISS

Areas of homogeneous gneiss without the bands, streaks and pods of basic material which characterise the migmatite are distributed throughout the Western Lewisian. Hornblende is generally absent but in other respects this gneiss is similar to the acid portion of the migmatite. The fresh rock is pink in colour and usually contains a proportion of biotite. Because of its massive and well-jointed character it tends to form steep and overhanging cliffs. These homogeneous gneisses are interpreted as orthogneisses originating as granitoid intrusions.

PEGMATITE

Veins of quartz-oligoclase-pegmatite (trondhjemite) up to 0.5 m thick cut the banding of the migmatitic gneiss and are also found cutting amphibolite. Concordant bands of pink quartzofeldspathic rock representing granulitised and

recrystallised pegmatite are locally abundant, for example in Allt Loch Innis nan Seangan [NG 935 335]. These quartzofeldspathic bands are the only rocks in the Western Lewisian that contain notable quantities of potash feldspar.

AMPHIBOLITE AND OTHER BASIC ROCKS

The Western Lewisian includes a high proportion of basic rock, typically a homogeneous granular amphibolite composed of coarse aggregates of hornblende and plagioclase, giving the rock a speckled black and white appearance. Locally the amphibolites have alternating bands rich in hornblende or plagioclase and these bodies may represent original layered basic intrusions. Many of the amphibolite bodies contain veins and patches of quartzofeldspathic material, in some exposures forming an interlacing network separating the amphibolite into angular fragments. Where the quartzofeldspathic material makes up a high proportion of the rock the outcrop has been mapped as migmatitic gneiss.

In the central part of the inlier basic masses show an irregular form and, in places, have cross-cutting relationships to the structures in the surrounding acid gneiss. In the marginal areas basic bodies are lenticular, with the lenses elongated parallel to the contact with the enclosing Moine. Also in the marginal areas, and in places elsewhere, highly deformed amphibolite has been altered to hornblende-schist, characterised by the development of cross-cutting porphyroblastic crystals of bronzy biotite.

Hornblende-pyroxene-granulites, some containing garnet or hypersthene, and variably retrogressed to garnet amphibolite, are found among the amphibolites. The largest mass of garnet-hornblende-pyroxene-granulite occurs northeast of Carn na Creige [NG 896 326] but the most accessible locality for these rocks is along the road cutting south of Eilean Donan Castle [NG 886 255]. Here garnet-hornblende-pyroxene-granulite containing blue quartz is associated with a lenticular mass of white feldspathic rock which is probably meta-anorthosite.

A number of fine-grained amphibolite dykes cross-cutting the banding in the gneisses, and generally less than 1.0 m thick, occur in the western Lewisian, for example, on the shore at Avernish [NG 843 261] and Nostie Bay [NG 854 264] (Sheet 71). The dykes were intruded after the formation of the migmatitic structure in the gneisses and at several localities [NG 887 290, NG 891 286] also cut across coarse-grained amphibolite which was evidently already pyroxene-granulite when the dykes were intruded. The dykes themselves have now been altered to amphibolite, but show no evidence of earlier high-grade mineralogy or texture, and thus appear to have been metamorphosed to amphibolite directly from basaltic igneous rocks. They are probably equivalent to the Scourie dykes of the foreland (cf. Clough in Peach et al., 1907).

ULTRABASIC ROCKS

A few small lenticular bodies of serpentinite occur in the Western Lewisian. The largest [at NG 890 335] has an outcrop up to 30 m wide, extends along the strike for at least 200 m and contains relics of olivine and pyroxene. The smaller masses have been partly or completely replaced by coarsely crystalline actinolite, talc, chlorite and carbonate.

METAMORPHIC AND STRUCTURAL HISTORY (see Table 1)

At the earliest recognisable stage in its development the Western Lewisian consisted of a migmatite complex composed of acid gneiss intimately mixed with bands and lenticles of basic rock. Acidic bodies, now represented by granodioritic gneiss, were intruded into the migmatite complex. Later, basic intrusions were emplaced. These bodies are seen to have a cross-cutting relationship, both to the migmatite banding and to the contacts between the migmatites and the granitic intrusions, for example near Loch Thollaidh [NG 896 302]. The migmatite complex, granodiorite and basic rocks were then metamorphosed in the granulite facies. This is the earliest metamorphic event for which there is textural and mineralogical evidence. Very well-preserved granulites are found among the amphibolites. In the acid gneisses most of the granulite-facies minerals have been recrystallised and are now represented by granoblastic aggregates although large relict feldspars containing retrogressive inclusions of white mica and clinozoisite are common. Acid granulites which have largely escaped retrogression occur in the Nostie area (Sheet 71E), for example at [NG 861 278]. Granulite facies metamor-

**Table 1** Sequence of events in the Western Lewisian and possible correlations (modified after Barber and May, 1975).

| | |
|---|---|
| D6$_L$ Monoclinal folds | |
| D5$_L$ Folding in thrust belt and Moine | Caledonian |
| D4$_L$ Mylonitisation and ESE-plunging lineation | |
| Amphibolite facies metamorphism<br>Growth of hornblende porphyroblasts | |
| D3$_L$ SE-plunging folds and rodding | ? Late Precambrian |
| D2$_L$ Interbanding of the Moine and the Lewisian | |
| D1$_L$ Interbanding of the Moine and the Lewisian | |
| Sedimentation of the Moine on the Lewisian basement | |
| Intrusion of basic dykes | Scourie dykes |
| Granulite facies metamorphism | Scourian |
| Intrusion of basic rocks | |
| Intrusion of granodiorite | ?Pre-Scourian |
| Formation of migmatite complex | |

D1$_L$ – D6$_L$: Deformation events in the Lewisian

phism was followed by the intrusion of basic dykes, an event which appears to be the last to affect the Western Lewisian before the deposition of the Moine. Intrusion of pegmatite veins probably took place at more than one stage during the formation of the Lewisian complex. Some pegmatites cut the large amphibolite bodies but all are in a much more granulitised condition than younger quartzofeldspathic veins which occur in the Moine, and locally in the Lewisian.

Most of the fold structures, lineations and planar fabrics found in the Western Lewisian have been assigned by Barber and May (1975) to deformation episodes that also affect the Moine (Table 1). Only small areas completely escaped deformation. The rocks least deformed during $D1_L$ to $D3_L$ occur in the central part of the inlier and it is here that original Lewisian textures and minerals have survived. The more strongly deformed rocks developed a foliar structure and underwent amphibolite facies metamorphism which ended with the growth of randomly orientated porphyroblasts of hornblende. A later phase of deformation ($D4_L$ and $D2_M$) profoundly affected the Moine and a few marginal areas of the Western Lewisian. In these areas the rocks were mylonitised and hornblende porphyroblasts were replaced by aggregates of biotite flakes forming pseudomorphs which are elongated parallel to the $D4_L$ ESE-plunging lineation. The central part of the inlier behaved as a rigid block during $D4_L$ and was only slightly deformed. The $D4_L$ lineation and mylonitic foliation can be correlated directly with the extensive development of mylonite in the thrust belt a short distance to the west (Barber, 1965). They can also be correlated with similar structures in mylonitised Cambrian quartzite further north, in Assynt (McLeish, 1971; Wilkinson et al., 1975) showing that $D4_L$ is almost certainly of Caledonian age. However, the earlier episodes ($D1_L - D3_L$) may be late Precambrian.

$D5_L$ structures (Table 1) are developed in mylonites west of the Moine Thrust and in the Moine east of the inlier but have not been found in the Western Lewisian. The final stage of deformation ($D6_L$) was the formation of small-scale monoclinal folds, commonly in conjugate sets. They are confined to the more laminated horizons in the inlier and formed under brittle conditions with jointing and faulting occuring in the adjoining more massive rocks.

## Eastern Lewisian

The large outcrop of Eastern Lewisian which occurs in the Glenelg district (Sheet 71E) extends eastwards and then southwards around a major fold closure in Moine rocks near Fern Villa [NG 887 229] occupying the ground on the southwest side of Loch Duich as far south as the margin of the Ratagain Complex and reappearing on the north-west side of the loch at Inverinate [NG 925 215]. The outcrop extends northwards from Inverinate, narrowing and wedging out entirely half way between the River Glennan and Loch Long (Figure 4). In the area north of Loch Duich the Eastern Lewisian lies, in the west, on a strip of extremely deformed rock (p.23) separating it from the Western Lewisian and, in the east, it is overlain by the Moine.

For descriptive purposes the rocks making up the Eastern Lewisian can be classified into:

(a) Metasediments
(b) Basic and ultrabasic rocks
(c) Hornblende and biotite gneisses and their blastomylonitic derivatives
(d) Pegmatite.

### METASEDIMENTS

Rocks derived from a sedimentary succession occupy a broad belt in the centre of the Eastern Lewisian (Figure 5). They are flanked by gneisses of igneous aspect and may lie in the core of a pre-Moine fold.

*Forsterite marble*    Exposures of marble are most commonly found immediately adjacent to the band of pelite which almost bisects the outcrop of the Eastern Lewisian. It is clear from the distribution of outcrops (Figure 5) that the marble forms a discontinuous band up to 50 m thick both above and below the garnet-biotite-schist which dips generally to the east. Small outcrops also occur within hornblende and biotite gneisses and away from the main outcrop of marble, for example on either side of the road at Carr Brae [NG 895 247].

In the field the marbles have a characteristic black weathered crust with a rough rasp-like surface due to the relative resistance to weathering of the contained silicate minerals, which project from the surface. Freshly broken surfaces are, in contrast, pure white, flecked with green. The silicate minerals, commonly concentrated in bands, range from individual crystals of forsterite or diopside the size of small peas to massive aggregates of diopside forming nodules a metre or more across. Each diopside nodule is separated from the surrounding marble by a sheath of dark green fibrous amphibole. A variety of angular rock inclusions such as hornblende gneiss and amphibolite also occur and may have once formed continuous bands within the marble. The mineral banding is commonly folded in a plastic fashion and the bands diverge around the nodules and inclusions to form an augen structure.

Thin sections show that the marbles are composed of equidimensional grains of calcite and dolomite in which are embedded a variety of silicate minerals, notably forsterite (partially serpentinised), diopside, phlogopite, chlorite and a mineral of the humite group. Sanders (1972) has identified clinohumite in a marble from the Glenelg area (Sheet 71W) and found it to be identical to the mineral described as chondrodite by Read and Double (1935).

The only previous chemical data for the marbles are four analyses in Moorhouse and Moorhouse (1983) of samples from Totaig Pier (Sheet 71E). These have now been complemented by 12 further analyses (Table 2) of the purer (i.e. carbonate-rich, silicate-poor) marbles from every major outcrop in both Sheets 71E and 72W. Isolated outcrops away from the main Totaig–Glen Beag marble belt, for example near Inverinate [NG 895 247], and in Area 2 [NH 0014 3041] were included. Details of sampling methods and analytical techniques are given in Rock (1985). Impure marbles, rich in Ca-Mg-Fe-silicate minerals (including those with large diopsidic nodules) were not analysed because these rocks are almost certainly removed, by metasomatism and reaction with silicate metasediments, from original carbonate sediment compositions. Despite macroscopic variations in colour, texture and silicate mineralogy, the new

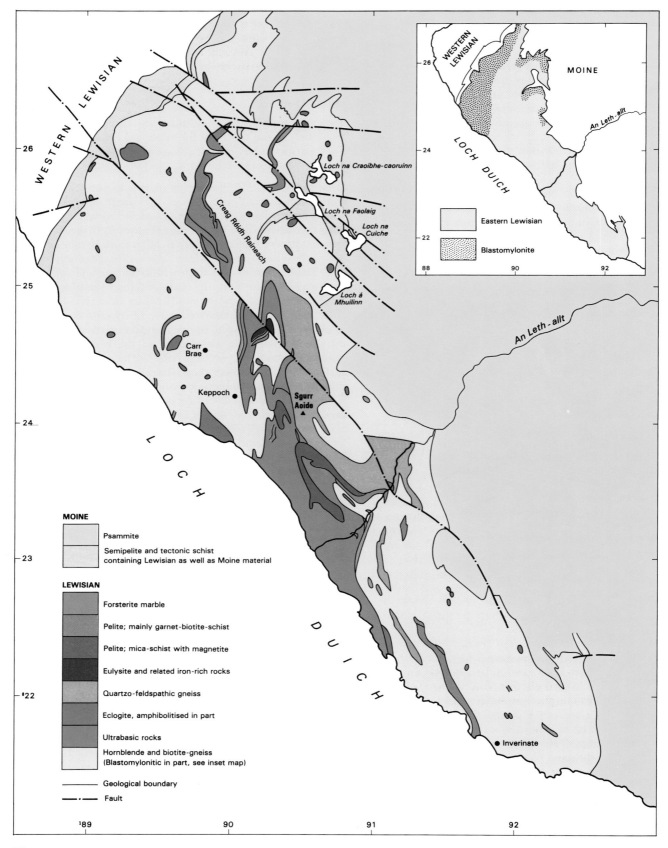

**MOINE**

Psammite

Semipelite and tectonic schist
containing Lewisian as well as Moine material

**LEWISIAN**

Forsterite marble

Pelite; mainly garnet-biotite-schist

Pelite; mica-schist with magnetite

Eulysite and related iron-rich rocks

Quartzo-feldspathic gneiss

Eclogite, amphibolitised in part

Ultrabasic rocks

Hornblende and biotite-gneiss
(Blastomylonitic in part, see inset map)

Geological boundary

Fault

Eastern Lewisian

Blastomylonite

**Figure 5**   Geological map of the Eastern Lewisian north-east of Loch Duich.

**Table 2**   Analyses of marbles from the Eastern Lewisian

| BGS No. | S71248 | S72677 | S72678 | S72679 | S72682 | S72684 | S72685 | S72688 | S72689 | S72690 | S72692 | S72693 |
|---|---|---|---|---|---|---|---|---|---|---|---|---|
| NGR [NG] | NH[0018 3041] | [9011 2458] | [9027 2388] | [9107 2347] | [9108 2231] | [9058 2097] | [9058 2093] | [8452 2028] | [8396 2002] | [8352 1696] | 8457 1633] | 8457 1633] |
| Sheet | 72W | 72W | 72W | 72W | 72W | 72W | 72W | 71E | 71E | 71E | 71E | 71E |
| $SiO_2$, % | 0.59 | 9.83 | 10.24 | 7.55 | 4.41 | 12.55 | 0.37 | 16.82 | 14.17 | 9.60 | 0.82 | 11.88 |
| $Al_2O_3$ | 0.08 | 0.73 | 0.65 | 0.90 | 0.52 | 0.85 | 0.02 | 1.20 | 0.77 | 0.31 | 0.08 | 1.15 |
| $Fe_2O_3$* | 0.51 | 2.61 | 1.11 | 1.83 | 1.50 | 0.61 | 0.69 | 1.29 | 1.59 | 0.55 | 0.69 | 1.63 |
| MgO | 19.87 | 17.75 | 16.28 | 19.3 | 20.46 | 14.72 | 20.42 | 20.30 | 19.48 | 21.01 | 20.52 | 18.94 |
| CaO | 31.72 | 30.94 | 34.20 | 28.6 | 29.12 | 35.81 | 30.53 | 28.26 | 29.15 | 31.13 | 30.61 | 31.74 |
| $Na_2O$ | bdl | 0.02 | 0.03 | 0.05 | 0.02 | 0.06 | bdl | 0.03 | 0.02 | 0.01 | bdl | 0.06 |
| $K_2O$ | 0.02 | 0.11 | 0.20 | 0.51 | 0.24 | 0.16 | 0.01 | 0.08 | 0.10 | 0.10 | 0.07 | 0.43 |
| LOI | 45.60 | 36.66 | 35.62 | 40.20 | 42.78 | 36.50 | 46.50 | 33.08 | 34.58 | 36.51 | 45.98 | 32.80 |
| $TiO_2$ | 0.01 | 0.04 | 0.05 | 0.06 | 0.04 | 0.06 | 0.02 | 0.06 | 0.06 | 0.03 | 0.02 | 0.09 |
| $P_2O_5$ | bdl | 0.01 | 0.01 | 0.01 | 0.01 | 0.01 | bdl | bdl | 0.01 | bdl | bdl | 0.05 |
| F | bdl | 0.10 | 0.13 | 0.10 | 0.07 | 0.15 | 0.04 | 0.10 | 0.11 | 0.09 | 0.04 | 0.15 |
| S | bdl | 0.13 | 0.06 | 0.02 | 0.06 | 0.05 | 0.02 | 0.03 | 0.07 | 0.02 | 0.02 | 0.05 |
| MnO | 0.09 | 0.28 | 0.11 | 0.15 | 0.14 | 0.07 | 0.10 | 0.09 | 0.13 | 0.08 | 0.10 | 0.15 |
| *Trace elements (ppm), in order of atomic number* | | | | | | | | | | | | |
| V | bdl | bdl | bdl | bdl | 20 | bdl | bdl | bdl | 10 | bdl | bdl | 10 |
| Cr | bdl | bdl | bdl | 10 | bdl | bdl | bdl | bdl | bdl | bdl | bdl | 10 |
| Co | — | 5 | 1 | 1 | 2 | bdl | bdl | 2 | 3 | bdl | 1 | 4 |
| Ni | bdl | bdl | bdl | bdl | 2 | 1 | bdl | 3 | 2 | bdl | bdl | 5 |
| Cu | bdl | 245 | 7 | bdl | 7 | bdl | 3 | bdl | 12 | bdl | bdl | 9 |
| Zn | 3 | 5 | 8 | 9 | 8 | 4 | 1 | 6 | 8 | 3 | 2 | 9 |
| Rb | bdl | 4 | 6 | 21 | 9 | 5 | 1 | 4 | 4 | 5 | 2 | 12 |
| Sr | 195 | 83 | 81 | 142 | 55 | 147 | 54 | 104 | 91 | 46 | 55 | 50 |
| Y | 2 | 2 | 1 | 3 | 2 | 2 | 2 | 2 | 2 | 1 | 3 | 4 |
| Zr | bdl | 3 | 4 | 8 | 5 | 7 | bdl | 6 | 7 | 2 | bdl | 7 |
| Nb | bdl | bdl | bdl | 1 | bdl | bdl | bdl | bdl | bdl | bdl | bdl | bdl |
| Sn | bdl | bdl | bdl | bdl | bdl | bdl | 2 | bdl | bdl | bdl | 1 | 1 |
| Ba | bdl | 50 | 60 | 40 | 70 | 180 | 10 | 50 | 80 | 20 | 20 | 120 |
| La | bdl | bdl | bdl | bdl | bdl | bdl | bdl | bdl | bdl | bdl | bdl | bdl |
| Ce | 10 | 20 | 10 | 10 | 10 | 20 | 10 | 10 | bdl | 10 | bdl | bdl |
| Pb | 2 | bdl | 1 | bdl | 1 | 1 | bdl | 1 | 5 | bdl | bdl | 1 |
| Th | bdl | bdl | bdl | 1 | bdl | bdl | bdl | bdl | bdl | bdl | bdl | bdl |
| U | bdl | 1 | bdl | 1 | 4 | bdl | bdl | bdl | 3 | bdl | 1 | 2 |

* Total Fe as $Fe_2O_3$. bdl = below detection limit. — = not analysed.
*Major elements* by Betaprobe, *trace elements* by XRF methods — analysts: A E Davis, D Hutchinson, T K Smith,
(BGS Analytical Chemistry Research Group). For further details, indication of reproducibility etc. see Rock (1986).

analyses in Table 2 are similar both to each other and to the four previous analyses. The major variation is in silicate impurities, but all the rocks are Mg-rich. The Mg and Ca contents of the present carbonate rocks (S71248, 72685, 72692) are very close to those of pure dolomite (21.7% MgO, 30.4% CaO), suggesting that the parent sediments immediately prior to metamorphism had been primary dolostones or completely dolomitised limestones. At least some of the calcite which now occurs in the less-pure marbles was probably generated by decarbonation of dolomite, in the well-known reaction series of siliceous dolomites (forsterite, diopside etc). The diopside nodules may have been formed from masses of chert which reacted with the dolomite during metamorphism. The inclusions of other rock types may have been derived from rocks marginal to the limestones or from bands within them. These rocks were disrupted during deformation of the marble. The discontinuous, lenticular nature of the marble is probably the result of the disruption of several continuous limestone bands during folding.

Chemically and mineralogically the marbles closely resemble those in the Lewisian of South Harris (Rock, 1985). The typical mineral assemblages (dolomite + minor calcite + serpentinised olivine + diopside + humite group minerals) are identical, and the whole-rock compositions virtually indistinguishable. By contrast, they differ from almost all other available analyses of marbles from the Lewisian inliers within the Moine, (Scardroy, Glen Strathfarrar, Shin-ness, Loch Monar, Loch Luichart) which are dolomite-poor calcite limestones (Rock, 1985). The Glenelg inlier is the only one in which dolostones are dominant over limestones.

In their extremely low contents of all trace elements, and especially Sr, the Sheet 72W marbles are typical not only of Lewisian marbles but of Archaean carbonate rocks the world over. Younger limestones and dolostones, e.g. from the Scottish Dalradian, have Sr contents 1–2 orders of magnitude higher (up to about 2000 ppm) in rocks of equivalent major element composition. Zr, Ce and Nb contents of the Lewisian are also notably lower (Rock et al., 1984, figs 4–6). The Sheet 72 marbles are particularly low in Sr, even from the Lewisian, because of the low tolerance of dolomite relative to calcite for Sr.

Some authors (e.g. Tucker, 1982) have suggested that, unlike Phanerozoic dolostones, which are secondary, ancient dolostones may represent primary dolomite-rich sediments. Textural evidence for the primary nature of Lewisian dolomite has been destroyed by metamorphism, but there is some chemical support for this idea from other parts of the Lewisian (Rock, 1985).

*Pelite; mainly garnet-biotite-schist*   Pelite (shown as garnet-biotite-gneiss on the 1:50 000 map) has been traced as a continuous band, associated with lenticular masses of marble, northwards from the shore of Loch Duich to Creag Reidh Raineach (Figure 5). Small isolated masses are also found within the hornblende and biotite gneisses. The typical pelite is a schist showing mineral banding and characterised by large mauve garnets, commonly more than 20 mm across, scattered in a fine-grained matrix of biotite, plagioclase and quartz with varying amounts of chlorite and muscovite. Barber (1968) has found scapolite in one section and rutile, zircon, graphite and iron ore as common accessory minerals. The garnet forms augen which are partly altered along cracks to chlorite and biotite.

The residual nature of the garnet suggests that the schist has been derived from a pre-existing coarser-grained garnetiferous rock which Sanders (1972) has found to be very locally preserved, for example at NG 905 233. Here and at other localities in the Glenelg area (Sheet 71E) garnet-kyanite-orthoclase-gneiss forms small patches, a metre or two across, which can be traced laterally into garnet-biotite-schist. In the field this gneiss is easily recognised by its striking red or lilac coloured garnets, which may account for as much as half the rock. Small blades of blue kyanite are generally visible in the pale grey, quartzofeldspathic matrix. The mineral assemblage is: Garnet-orthoclase-plagioclase-quartz-biotite-kyanite, plus accessories: Rutile-ilmenite-graphite-apatite-allanite. Sanders (1972) also reports the presence of omphacite in a specimen of the gneiss from NG 853 234 (Sheet 71E).

Only one analysis of these rocks, for major elements only, has been published previously (Guppy and Thomas, 1931). The original powder of this sample (S13250) has now been reanalysed, along with three other samples of kyanite gneiss also from Sheet 71E (Table 3). The old and new major element values for S13250 proved to be virtually identical, except for $Na_2O$, where the old (chloroplatinate method) determination can be assumed to be less accurate. The coexistence of kyanite and K-feldspar without muscovite indicates that the rocks have passed above the P–T limits of the reaction:

$$muscovite + quartz = kyanite + K\text{-}feldspar.$$

There is little evidence of significant retrogression in the analysed samples, although other outcrops in the area show development of muscovite by shimmerisation of kyanite.

Chemically and petrographically, these kyanite-gneisses resemble the Lewisian kyanite-gneisses of South Harris, reflecting the same affinities as the Sheet 72W marbles. The kyanite-gneisses in Table 3 are readily distinguished chemically from Moine kyanite-schists by their much higher contents of V, Cr, Ni, Cu, Zn, Fe, Mg and lower Y, Nb (Rock et al., 1986). Moine kyanite-schists also tend to lack allanite and rutile, invariably lack graphite and these differences, extending to several immobile elements, can be assumed to reflect differences in original sedimentary compositions. Dalradian kyanite-schists can carry an almost identical mineral assemblage to these Lewisian rocks (except perhaps for allanite), but again the Lewisian rocks are notably richer in Fe, Mg, Ca and poorer in Y, Nb, Rb, K, Al (Rock et al., 1986). Clearly, therefore, these Glenelg kyanite-gneisses represent a distinctive group of ancient pelitic sediments, richer in Mg and in various accessory minerals than younger Scottish kyanite-bearing pelites. This richness in Mg reflects a similar richness in the associated marbles, and suggests that the parent pelitic sediments were themselves dolomitic.

**Table 3** Analyses of kyanite-gneisses from the Eastern Lewisian from near Glenelg

| BGS No. | U2340 | U2341 | S7939 | S13250 |
|---|---|---|---|---|
| NGR [NG] | [832 173] | [832 173] | [832 173] | [860 160] |
| Sheet | 71E | 71E | 71E | 71E |
| $SiO_2$, % | 59.8 | 55.5 | 59.1 | 56.4 |
| $Al_2O_3$ | 18.21 | 17.59 | 17.78 | 18.88 |
| $Fe_2O_3$* | 9.01 | 13.06 | 10.57 | 11.84 |
| MgO | 4.09 | 5.04 | 5.91 | 5.30 |
| CaO | 2.19 | 1.45 | 1.59 | 2.21 |
| $Na_2O$ | 1.00 | 0.85 | 0.66 | 0.84 |
| $K_2O$ | 2.24 | 3.34 | 3.00 | 2.63 |
| $TiO_2$ | 1.14 | 1.00 | 1.08 | 1.06 |
| $P_2O_5$ | 0.08 | 0.06 | 0.11 | 0.08 |
| MnO | 0.06 | 0.11 | 0.09 | 0.09 |
| *Trace elements (ppm), in order of atomic number* | | | | |
| V | 293 | 221 | 252 | 253 |
| Cr | 261 | 230 | 240 | 236 |
| Ni | 78 | 72 | 89 | 120 |
| Cu | 40 | 57 | 57 | 79 |
| Zn | 156 | 183 | 172 | 145 |
| Rb | 84 | 108 | 105 | 96 |
| Sr | 170 | 133 | 167 | 203 |
| Y | 16 | 29 | 23 | 28 |
| Zr | 108 | 118 | 109 | 102 |
| Nb | 12 | 9 | 8 | 12 |
| Ba | 586 | 846 | 756 | 546 |
| Ce | 28 | 48 | 43 | 60 |
| Pb | 10 | 11 | 11 | 16 |

* Total Fe as $Fe_2O_3$
Analyses by conventional XRF techniques at Lancaster University. For further details, indications of reproducibility, etc, see Rock et al. (1986).

*Pelite; mica-schist with magnetite*  Thin bands of magnetite-bearing mica-schist occur throughout the outcrop of the hornblende and biotite gneiss but the most extensive developments are associated with the pelite (garnet-biotite-schist) of Sgurr Aoidhe (Figure 5). In the field it is distinguished from garnet-biotite-schist by its darker colour and by the presence of small red garnets instead of the large mauve garnets which are so characteristic of the latter. In the major outcrop on Sgurr Aoidhe the magnetite-bearing mica-schist contains large numbers of quartz and quartzo-feldspathic bands and lenticles extending along the foliation. The mineral assemblage is: Biotite-muscovite-garnet-quartz-plagioclase-magnetite, plus accessory zircon. Magnetite is sufficiently abundant to be regarded as a major constituent and indicates that the original argillaceous sediment was iron-rich. Thin sections show that a coarse-grained rock produced during an early period of metamorphism was subsequently granulitised with the production of augen structures.

*Eulysite and related iron-rich rocks*  Tilley (1936) described an occurrence of various rare iron-rich rocks, some containing abundant fayalite and therefore classed as eulysite, from the Eastern Lewisian at Druideag Lodge (Sheet 71E). Similar rocks have been reported by Barber (1968) from the north-east side of Loch Duich.

The major occurrence lies just within the outcrop of the pelite, and forms the summit of a rocky knoll [NG 902 246] overlooking the road near Carr Brae. The characteristic eulysite is a dense black rock with crystals of fayalite projecting from the weathered surface. On freshly broken surfaces the olivine is brown and translucent with a resinous lustre and is associated with bright red garnet. The eulysites are banded with magnetite-rich layers, projecting as ribs on weathered surfaces, alternating with silicate-rich layers. The banding is parallel to the banding in the adjacent metasediments. Across the depression which separates this knoll from the foot of Creag Reidh Raineach is a small excavation in iron-rich rocks composed of an amphibole, as coarse, yellowish translucent bladed crystals, associated with bright red garnet.

Smaller occurrences of eulysitic rocks are found at NG 905 251 and NG 902 253. Sanders (1972) has investigated the mineralogy of the occurrence at NG 902 253 and others from the area west of Loch Duich (Sheet 71E) and finds that the rock types fall very broadly into two groups. One includes those rocks which are essentially anhydrous and whose mineralogy is dominated by fayalite, iron hypersthene, hedenbergite or pyroxmangite, while in the second group cummingtonite and other amphiboles are abundant.

The mineral assemblages found by Sanders (1972) at NG 902 253 are:
1 Iron hypersthene-fayalite-garnet-magnetite-apatite. This is found in a coarse-grained granular rock traversed by veins of fibrous amphibole (?grunerite) growing perpendicular to the vein wall.
2 Garnet-cummingtonite-magnetite-quartz.
3 Garnet-cummingtonite-magnetite-quartz-actinolite-clinopyroxene. In this rock the amphiboles have developed at the expense of the pyroxene.

An intimate association with pelite and marble leaves little doubt that the eulysitic rocks are derived from sediments and the alternation of magnetite-rich and silicate-rich bands is probably relict bedding. Sanders (1972) recognises, on the basis of petrography, three phases of crystallisation:
1 Formation of anhydrous eulysites.
2 Entry of water in various amounts with formation of coarse amphibole in equilibrium with any residual anhydrous phases.
3 Late retrogression with growth of fibrous amphibole.

*Quartzofeldspathic gneiss*    Quartzofeldspathic gneiss crops out in a broad belt extending north-westwards from An Leth-allt to the southern end of Creag Reidh Raineach (Figure 5). It overlies the pelite but on Creag Reidh Raineach it passes round a large fold closure and continues as a thin band below the pelite as far as Keppoch. Several smaller outcrops of a similar rock type, generally associated with pelite or marble, occur elsewhere (Figure 5).

The quartzofeldspathic gneiss is a pink, fine-grained rock with a well-marked banded structure which is commonly folded and crossed by a secondary cleavage. It contains many concordant bands and lenticles of quartz and feldspar and is cut by pegmatite veins. Thin sections show that it is composed of quartz, microcline and plagioclase with minor or accessory muscovite, biotite, magnetite, epidote, allanite and zircon. The magnetite occurs as euhedral crystals arranged in bands and the zircon as small rounded grains. The textures show stages in the breakdown of a coarse-grained rock to a finer-grained one.

The quartzofeldspathic gneiss is granitic in appearance, and an intrusive origin is suggested by the occurrence of dark hornblendic patches, up to a few centimetres in size, which may represent xenoliths. The only evidence of the sedimentary origin (feldspathic sandstone or arkose) for the quartzofeldspathic gneiss, apart from its association with undoubted metasedimentary rocks, is the presence of well-rounded grains of zircon.

BASIC AND ULTRABASIC ROCKS

Scattered through the outcrop of the Eastern Lewisian, mainly in the area mapped as hornblende and biotite gneiss, are large numbers of small masses of basic and ultrabasic rock. The larger outcrops are shown in Figure 5, but in addition there are many smaller bands, lenticles, nodules and irregular masses which it is impossible to represent on the scale of the map. For the purpose of description they are classified under three headings:
1 Eclogites and their derivatives
2 Pyroxenites and other ultrabasic rocks
3 Non-eclogitic amphibolites.

*Eclogites and their derivatives*    The rock type from the Eastern Lewisian which has attracted most attention from mineralogists and petrologists is eclogite. The first occurrence of eclogite in the British Isles was recorded at Totaig on the south-western side of Loch Duich opposite Dornie (Sheet 71E) by Teall (1891) and later accounts, some dealing with specific aspects of eclogite petrology, are given by Clough (*in* Peach et al., 1910), Alderman (1936) Mercy and O'Hara (1968) and Sanders (1972).

Eclogite is conspicuous in the field because of its bright green pyroxene studded with garnets which are commonly 20 mm or more in diameter. Completely unaltered eclogite is comparatively rare but rocks which show by their texture or mineralogy that they have been retrogressively derived from eclogite, are common. The general distribution of these rocks is shown in Figure 5. They occur among the hornblende and biotite gneisses as bands ranging up to several metres in thickness. The larger (greater than 2 m) bodies of eclogitic rock tend to form isolated exposures so that their shape and relationship to the surrounding rocks are not seen. Some occurrences show an alternation of bands rich in garnet and those rich in pyroxene. Where the relationships can be seen, for example at Keppoch [NG 903 245], the bands are parallel to the margins of the eclogite and also to the banding in the adjacent gneiss. Eclogitic rocks have not been observed to transgress the mineral banding of the hornblende and biotite gneiss.

The eclogite consists of equidimensional crystals of omphacite with embayed margins and large rounded or subidiomorphic garnets. Primary brown hornblende is found in some sections and small amounts of interstitial quartz and plagioclase are commonly present. Rutile is a characteristic accessory.

Barber (1968) found only one occurrence [at NG 903 236] of eclogite in the area north-east of Loch Duich where the minerals show no signs of alteration; the majority show at least some retrogressive effects of the following types:
1 Symplectisation
2 Amphibolitisation
3 Cataclasis.

According to Alderman (1936) the symplectic structure is due to the breakdown of omphacite into an aggregate of diopside and plagioclase. Zones of amphibolitisation transect the symplectic structure showing that the crystallisation of amphibole occurred later than and was independent of the formation of symplectite. The characteristic mineral of the new amphibolite assemblage is a blue-green hornblende which is distinctly different in its optical properties from the primary brown hornblende. Omphacite is progressively replaced by hornblende and garnet by aggregates of hornblende, biotite, and epidote. Whole outcrops of eclogite rock are found in which the pyroxene is completely amphibolitised; in others the development of amphibolite is patchy with an obvious relationship to the shape of the body or to its margins. In the field the amphibolite is a dark greenish grey, fine-grained, with relict garnet and contrasts strongly with the bright greens and reds and the coarse granular texture of the eclogite it has replaced.

Among the mylonitic rocks which extend northwards from the shore of Loch Duich (Figure 5 inset) are bands, sometimes no more than 25 mm thick, of a fine-grained foliated greenish black rock studded with bright red garnets. Thin sections show that this rock is an amphibolitised eclogite which has been affected by extreme cataclasis. The relict garnets contain characteristic inclusions of rutile. All the minerals have been granulated and streaked out into bands which diverge round relict crystals and crystal aggregates. Some recrystallisation took place during and later than the cataclasis and the rock can therefore be classified as a blastomylonite.

*Pyroxenites and other ultrabasic rocks*    A nodule of pyroxenite (websterite) about 1.2 m in diameter is enclosed in mylonitic hornblende and biotite gneiss at the roadside at Carr Brae [NG 890 259]. The rock, which has a very striking appearance, is composed of large (10 mm) crystals of bright green diopside mingled with schillerised grey orthopyroxene, the whole being studded with large bronzy mica flakes, which become more abundant towards the margins of the mass where they form a micaceous sheath. Sanders (1972) also reports the presence of a little olivine.

A nodule of olive-green saccharoidal rock with scattered biotite flakes occurs in biotite-gneiss in the bank of An Leth-allt just downstream from the old road bridge [NG 908 231]. Radial outgrowths of dark green bladed actinolite crystals separate the nodule from the surrounding gneiss. A thin section shows that the rock is a pyroxenite composed of diopside with interstitial biotite. Pyroxenite nodules have also been found at Inverinate [NG 922 219, NG 918 216].

A large exposure of talc-tremolite-chlorite-rock occurs at the eastern end of Loch na Craoibhg-caoruinn [NG 907 258]. It has a limonite-stained, scaly weathered surface and joints widened by weathering. Its relationships to the surrounding rocks are not seen but it lies close to the Moine–Lewisian boundary. Pseudomorphs after olivine are recognisable in thin section and the rock is probably an altered peridotite. Bands of talc-bearing rock also occur in a road cutting at Inverinate [NG 919 218].

*Non-eclogitic amphibolite*    The eclogites shown on the geological map (Figure 5) are largely amphibolitised but there are many small bands and lenses of amphibolite (too small to be shown on Figure 5) which, although they are sometimes associated with eclogitic rocks, show none of the diagnostic minerals and textures which have enabled the latter to be identified even when highly modified by later deformation. Although all the non-eclogitic amphibolites have a similar stable mineral assemblage (hornblende + plagioclase + biotite + epidote + quartz + accessory sphene) their textures suggest that rocks of two different origins are present:

1   Amphibolite derived from a coarse-grained rock, possibly a pyroxene granulite or a coarser-grained amphibolite.

2   Amphibolite derived from medium-grained rock, showing no evidence of an earlier metamorphic history, and possibly derived directly from an igneous rock.

No cross-cutting relationships have been found but in other respects these rocks resemble the amphibolite dykes of the Western Lewisian.

### HORNBLENDE- AND BIOTITE-GNEISS

Hornblende- and biotite-gneisses, together with their blasto-mylonitic derivatives, constitute the major part of the outcrop of the Eastern Lewisian (Figure 5). Some of the gneiss has a coarse-banded structure, arising from the alternation of quartzofeldspathic and ferromagnesian layers, and contains streaks, bands and lenticles of basic and ultrabasic rock already described. This type of development, which is well exposed in An Leth-allt above the old road bridge, resembles the migmatitic gneiss of the Western Lewisian. Another characteristic rock type is a laminated gneiss with alternating layers, only 1 to 4 mm thick, of quartzofeldspathic and ferro-magnesian minerals. In this rock the mica flakes and hornblende crystals are well orientated giving a planar fabric lying parallel to the layering and allowing the rock to be split easily along the foliation planes even when these are folded. The gneisses are composed of quartz, oligioclase, biotite, hornblende and epidote with accessory sphene and magnetite. Apart from a rare occurrence of antiperthite potash feldspar is absent.

In his account of the neighbouring area of Glenelg, Clough (*in* Peach et al., 1910) described fine-grained microgranulitic rocks containing larger crystals of garnet, hornblende and feldspar, occurring as bands among the other rocks of the Eastern Lewisian. In the same area Ramsay (1957) noted that these rocks might, at first sight, be mistaken for flow-banded andesites or rhyolites but both workers recognised their mylonitic affinities.

Similar mylonitic bands are found among the hornblende- and biotite-gneiss of the Loch Duich area and their general distribution is indicated on the map (Figure 5, inset). They are characterised by a groundmass composed of quartz, feldspar, hornblende, biotite, epidote and sphene which is laminated and extremely fine grained (0.1 mm). Embedded in this groundmass are a great variety of large crystals and crystal aggregates forming augen structures. Many of the rock types of the Eastern Lewisian have their mylonitic representatives. However, from the nature of the materials of which the larger areas of mylonitic rock are composed it is clear that they were largely derived from hornblende- and biotite-gneiss. Rock fragments seen in the field and relict mineral grains seen in thin section indicate that the parent gneisses contained bands of eclogite, amphibolite and pegmatite. The annealed contacts between grains in the groundmass, the subparallel arrangement of mica flakes and spongy outgrowths round relict grains of epidote provide evidence of recrystallisation following granulitisation. An occurrence of small stable spongy garnets within the groundmass suggest that this recrystallisation reached the garnet grade of metamorphism. Although the extent of syntectonic recrystallisation is uncertain the microgranulitic rocks are provisionally classified as blastomylonite (Higgins, 1971). Later modification of the texture is seen where mylonitic banding is folded with biotite flakes orientated parallel to the axial plane.

PEGMATITE

Clough (*in* Peach et al., 1910, p.20) recognised two types of pegmatite within the Lewisian of the Glenelg district (Sheet 71E): '... the greater part of it is in a granulitic condition and ... crossed by foliation planes ... while in the pegmatitic material in the adjacent Moine rocks the feldspar is not often granulitic and foliation planes are but rarely present ... it seems probable that most of the pegmatitic material at present existing in the Lewisian Gneiss in a granulitic condition has been introduced therein during some period of metamorphism which passed away before the beds which are now represented by the Moine rocks were deposited. The pegmatites which were subsequently introduced both into the Moine rocks and the Lewisian Gneiss series, apparently in connection with a later period of folding and metamorphism, have not been so often or so completely granulitised ...'. Later work in the Inverinate area by Clifford (1957) has also revealed the presence of two generations of pegmatite, the earlier granulitised type being extensively developed.

METAMORPHIC AND STRUCTURAL HISTORY

The geological history of the Eastern Lewisian is summarised in Table 4. The outcrop of the Eastern Lewisian consists of a central area of metasediments surrounded by hornblende- and biotite-gneiss. At the earliest recognisable stage the hornblende- and biotite-gneiss appears to have been a migmatite complex resembling the migmatitic gneiss of the Western Lewisian. The lack of extensive migmatisation of the metasediments suggests that the migmatite complex predates the deposition of the sediments (a basement and cover relationship). The general absence of eclogite from the outcrop of the metasediments suggests that the intrusion of the early basic rocks may also predate the deposition of the sediments.

The common survival of high-grade rock types and mineral assemblages indicates that the migmatite complex, early igneous intrusions and sediments were subjected to eclogite facies metamorphism. Sanders (1972) concludes, on the basis of microprobe analyses of various minerals, that the pyroxene-granulites in the Western Lewisian equilibrated under different conditions from the eclogites in the Eastern Lewisian, and probably at a lower pressure and/or higher temperature than the eclogites. This could be the result of a pressure and temperature gradient during a single period of metamorphism but Sanders et al., (1984) have obtained mineral and whole rock Sm-Nd isochrons showing that the eclogite equilibrated at just over 1000 Ma. The eclogite

**Table 4** Sequence of events in the Eastern Lewisian (modified after Barber, 1968).

| |
|---|
| $D6_L$ Monoclinal folding |
| $D5_L$ Asymmetrical folding |
| $D4_L$ Reclined folding and ESE-plunging lineation. Eastern Lewisian overthrust on to Western Lewisian. Mylonitisation. Recrystallisation, amphibolite facies |
| $D1_L$ Isoclinal folding and granulitisation. Amphibolite facies metamorphism |
| Sedimentation of the Moine on the Lewisian basement |
| ? Intrusion of basic igneous rocks |
| Eclogite facies metamorphism |
| Deposition of sediments |
| Emplacement of basic and ultrabasic igneous bodies |
| Formation of migmatite complex |

$D2_L$ and $D3_L$ structures which occur in the Western Lewisian have not been recognised in the Eastern Lewisian

facies metamorphism thus appears to be of Grenville age and therefore much younger than the inferred Scourian-age granulite-facies metamorphism of the Western Lewisian. There is, at present, no evidence to show that the eclogite facies metamorphism was superimposed on earlier granulite facies assemblages.

Most of the amphibolites in the Eastern Lewisian have been derived from eclogite but there are a few which show no evidence of an earlier metamorphic history and could have been derived directly from an igneous rock which was intruded into the complex after the eclogite facies metamorphism. It must be emphasised, however, that cross-cutting relationships with the adjacent rocks have not been found. Further work on these possible post-eclogite basic intrusions is required so that their significance in relation to the age of sedimentation of the Moine and the Grenville age of the eclogite facies metamorphism can be assessed.

It is extremely difficult to compile a satisfactory structural history for the Eastern Lewisian. Firstly, all the linear structures and all the minor fold axes plunge in an easterly direction, and all the minor fold axial planes dip in the same direction. This makes it difficult to separate structures belonging to different phases on the basis of their orientation. Secondly, fold structures and their associated linear and foliar structures change radically in style and appearance as they pass from one rock type to another. In spite of these difficulties several periods of deformation, all postdating the deposition of the Moine, can be recognised (Table 4). The earliest, $D1_L$, gave rise to isoclinal folds of the mineral banding, widespread granulitisation and, locally, the formation of blastomylonite.

After the folding the rocks were subjected to amphibolite facies metamorphism which affected some parts of the Eastern Lewisian more than others. In the central part of the outcrop, mainly in the area occupied by the metasediments, the effects are relatively slight. Outside this area, towards the upper and lower margins of the complex, the rocks are affected to a major extent by deformation and recrystallisation. This difference in degree of deformation is responsible for the contrast between the coarsely banded and the laminated biotite- and hornblende-gniess. In the marginal areas evidence of the earlier high-grade metamorphic conditions is only seen in relict rock fragments, mineral aggregates and individual relict minerals among the highly altered gneisses. Notable among these relicts are the eclogites which have survived through all the subsequent phases of deformation and changes in pressure and temperature. They are also so distinctive in mineralogy that they can still be recognised among the other rock types by the characteristic garnets with rutile inclusions, even when the rock is in the condition of a blastomylonite and the minerals of the groundmass have been completely altered to those stable in the amphibolite facies.

$D2_L$ and $D3_L$ structures, which occur in the Western Lewisian, have not been recognised in the Eastern Lewisian.

The $D4_L$ deformation was responsible for the large-scale reclined folding which forms a conspicuous feature of the structure of the Eastern Lewisian. The amphibolite facies of metamorphism was maintained during and subsequent to this phase of folding as hornblende and biotite crystals are oriented in the axial planes and elongated parallel to the axes of folds belonging to this phase of deformation. Evidence is presented later (p.30) showing that the strip of highly deformed rocks between the Western and Eastern Lewisian marks the course of a major slide (ductile thrust) on which the Eastern Lewisian was overthrust onto the Western Lewisian during $D4_L$.

The $D5_L$ deformation locally produced asymmetrical folds and, in the more micaceous bands, a crenulation cleavage. A few small-scale monoclines ($D6_L$) have been recorded in well-foliated and platy rocks. The development of chlorite from biotite in rocks showing these structures indicates that the grade of metamorphism was declining during $D5_L$ and $D6_L$.

## LEWISIAN OF AREA 2

Lewisian rocks, recognised by their distinctive mineralogy, form numerous concordant bands, rarely more than 100 m thick, within the Moine of Area 2 (Figure 4). The bands are believed to be slices of pre-Moine basement, which have been brought into their present position within the Moine succession by movement along ductile thrusts (slides). They have all been strongly affected by post-Moine deformation and metamorphism which has obscured any distinction between 'Western' and 'Eastern' Lewisian that may have been present originally and there is, therefore, no attempt to classify them on this basis.

The Lewisian bands have sharply defined boundaries which are generally parallel to the internal layering and to the foliation in the adjoining Moine. Some of the bands are very impersistent and cannot be traced along strike for more than a few metres; others run continuously for several kilometres. For example the band on the east side of Carn Bad a'Chreamha [NG 932 270] can be followed southwards, displaced by a few minor faults, for 5 km to where it joins with the Lewisian of the Glenelg inlier (Figure 4). Lewisian rocks locally form several distinct bands lying only a few metres apart and in the Allt Coireag Searrach [NH 0040 3165] a single band is seen to bifurcate, the branches, 1 m and 2 m thick, being separated by Moine psammite

The dominant Lewisian rock type is a hornblende-gneiss made up of dark-coloured hornblendic layers, generally a few millimetres to a few centimetres thick, alternating with pale feldspathic layers. It has a flaggy or schistose structure allowing it to disintegrate into small slabs and flakes. It weathers more readily than the Moine rocks and outcrops are commonly marked by green grassy areas contrasting with the adjacent Moine country which is characterised by massive joint-bounded crags with intervening hollows filled with moss and heather. In places the gneiss resembles Moine psammite but close examination reveals the presence of hornblendic laminae. In addition to hornblende the principal minerals are plagioclase, quartz, epidote and biotite. Clinopyroxene and microcline also occur locally and may be abundant, for example on the western slope of Glen a' Choire Dhomhain [NG 9957 3253].

The hornblende-gneiss almost invariably contains bands and pods of amphibolite and hornblendite, usually with a mineral fabric lying parallel to the foliation of the adjoining gneiss. At some localities hornblende has been extensively replaced by biotite and the basic rocks are represented by a coarse-grained lustrous black schist (biotitite) containing relict crystals of hornblende or larger pods of amphibolite. A few of the Lewisian bands, generally less than 10 m thick, consist almost entirely of biotite.

Marble is a prominent constituent of the eastern facies of the Glenelg inlier and serpentinite bodies occur in both facies; both rock types have also been located amongst the small inliers of Area 2. An isolated exposure of pure white coarsely crystalline marble occurs in a small stream in Coire Shlat [NH 0018 3041] (for analysis see Table 2). A mass of serpentinite approximately 17 m wide is exposed in Allt a'Glas-choire [NG 9880 2934]. The eastern contact, marked by about 30 cm of talc, is concordant with the foliation in the adjoining quartz-biotite-rock. It is not seen in contact with other Lewisian rocks but occurs in a zone where Lewisian slices are very common. The fresh serpentinite is dark grey-green in colour and contains abundant relics of olivine, randomly orientated crystals of talc and a few pods of talc up to 10 cm in length. Weathering has produced a soft pale brown crust about 5 mm thick.

At a number of localities (p.59) unusual sodic rocks forming irregularly shaped discordant masses have formed by the metasomatic replacement of Moine psammite or Lewisian gneiss. They contain pyroxene and amphibole and those developed in the Moine could be mistaken for Lewisian inliers, especially where the field relationships are obscure. However, the metasomatic rocks can be distinguished petrographically by the abundance of albite and the presence of sodic pyroxene.

## LEWISIAN OF AREA 3

The Coire nan Gall area was originally mapped by Clifford (1957) who applied the term 'Lewisianoid' to rocks of Lewisian character but in a structural position which he considered anomalous. The presence of Lewisian rocks has been confirmed (unpublished work by Harris and Fleuty) and remapping has shown that much of the "Coire na Gall Series", considered by Clifford to be part of the Moine, is also Lewisian. The outcrop of the Lewisian has, therefore, been found to be much more extensive than previously thought and the Moine–Lewisian boundary has been completely revised (Figure 4).

The Lewisian consists mainly of hornblende-bearing acid gneiss and amphibolite, a notable feature of both being the common presence of clinopyroxene. At most localities feldspathic material is interbanded on all scales with layers in which amphibole is more or less abundant. The banding may be well defined with sharp contacts between layers or less well defined with gradational contacts. Granulitised pegmatite is abundant. Lenticular bodies of coarse-grained hornblendite, ranging from a few millimetres up to 1.0 m × 0.5 m in cross-section, are scattered throughout the Lewisian. Other types of ultramafic rock occur in a few places, for example near the summit of Sgurr an Airgid [NG 938 230] where there is an exposure of rock composed of actinolite, chlorite, talc and iron-oxide. Metasediments are represented by bands of marble and associated calcsilicate rocks containing diopside and tremolite in Allt Ghlomaich [NH 000 266] and by calcsilicate rock with abundant scapolite on the north side of the River Elchaig [NG 998 268]. Pelitic rocks which form such a prominent part of the Eastern Lewisian of Area 1, have not been reported nor have recognisable relics of eclogite although some of the amphibolite may be totally altered eclogite. The pyroxene found in the amphibolite and acid gneiss appears, from its textural relationships, to be the product of late recrystallisation and is probably not a remnant of a granulite or eclogite facies metamorphism of Lewisian age.

Problems arise locally in differentiating, in the field, between Lewisian acid gneiss which has been subjected to severe tectonic reworking and feldspathic Moine psammite. It is probable that there has been some tectonic homogenisation of the two rock types at their mutual junction but the extent of this mixing is not thought to be significant at the scale of mapping (1:10 000). The distribution of Lewisian rocks was determined on the basis of the presence of amphibole and, in general, acid feldspathic rocks in which it is lacking have been excluded from the Lewisian, although the precise position of the boundary with the Moine may be uncertain. The intimate interfolding of the Lewisian and Moine and other structural features are described later (p.34).

## LEWISIAN OF AREA 4

Hornblende- and pyroxene-bearing schists and gneisses which resemble rocks forming Lewisian inliers elsewhere on Sheet 72W are widely but sparsely distributed in the Shielbridge area, where they occur chiefly as narrow lenses or lenticles within the Moine succession. Simony (1973)

reported Lewisian lens-shaped bodies in the pelitic rocks of Sgurr Mhic Bharraich [NG 924 173] and as narrow continuous outcrops (up to 3.5 km long and 150 m wide) occurring in an arcuate zone extending from Allt a Choire Chaoil [NG 943 154] to the northern slopes of Beinn Aoidhdailean [NG 886 148].

The most common rock types are hornblende-schist and acid to intermediate gneisses which are generally hornblendic. These are associated at some localities with marble and calcsilicate rock containing diopside, talc, tremolite-actinolite and phlogopite. As an example, a band some 180 m long and 45 m wide containing these lithologies crops out in the valley of the Allt a' Chruinn, where it is well exposed in the stream bed at locality [NG 955 192]. Simony (1973) recorded forsterite and scapolite in the marble. A lens of serpentinite 200 m long occurs in a band of Lewisian rocks at a locality [NG 914 137] NW of Sgurr Leac nan Each and there is a pod of similar rock on the western peak of the Bealach a' Chasain valley [NG 890 142]. In the Sgurr Mhic Bharraich area [NG 90 17 and 91 17] and on the west side of Glen Shiel [NG 947 166] some of the pelites and semipelites closely associated with the hornblendic rocks may be Lewisian (Simony, 1973). East of Morvich [NG 961 211] a row of five boudins, up to 3 m long, of eclogite and garnetiferous hornblende-schist, too small to be shown on Sheet 72W, can be traced in the margin of pelite against psammite from just north of the river [NG 970 211] to the Glen Lichd road [NG 967 210].

In many of the bands and lenses noted above the Lewisian rocks are interbanded with typical Moine psammite and semipelite, particularly near their margins. The interleaved strata are folded by $D2_L$ folds (see p.15 for discussion of $D1_L$ to $D3_L$). Simony (1973) notes that the rocks were almost completely recrystallised during $D2_L$, but that traces of an earlier cataclasis remain. However, on the north side of Loch Shiel [at NG 943 187], an almost rectangular mass of Lewisian about 250 m long contains a core of very coarse foliated and non-foliated hornblende-plagioclase-zoisite rock which passes outwards into a hornblende-schist margin against Moine pelite and semipelite. The hornblende-schist appears to be a tectonic derivative of the core rock (Simony, 1973).

## LEWISIAN OF AREA 5

Lewisian rocks were originally mapped by C T Clough in the valley of the Allt Coire Mhalagain [NG 925 100]. They comprise a poorly exposed band about 500 m long and 30 to 40 m wide of hornblende-bearing acid gneiss thinly interleaved with semipelite and psammite of Moine aspect. The presence of such rocks within the Morar Division supports the view that there is not a simple stratigraphical succession in this area and that there may be thrust repetitions similar to those north of Glen Elchaig (p.26).

## LEWISIAN OF AREA 6

Bands and pods of Lewisian rocks occur in Glen Shiel and at the head of Loch Hourn. On the north side of Glen Shiel a band, some 10 m wide, of marble, calc-schist, tremolite rock

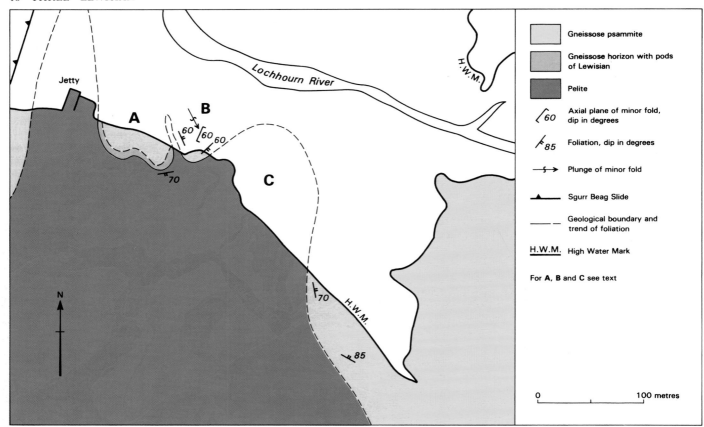

**Figure 6**  Large-scale map of the gneissose psammite with Lewisian pods and pelite, Kinloch Hourn.

and hornblende-gneiss can be traced for about 400 m up the hillside from the WNW-trending fault [NG 004 138]. It is flanked on both sides by gneissose psammite. At the eastern contact the band of hornblende-gneiss is interleaved in places with micaceous psammite. South of the fault part of the same band can be seen in a stream bed [NG 008 136] about 60 m north of the road (Sheet 72W). South of the River Shiel lenses and bands of similar rocks extend southwards for nearly 2 km, and are aligned parallel to, and east of, the trace of the Sgurr Beag Slide.

At the head of Loch Hourn, Lewisian rocks crop out in two fold closures (A and B on Figure 6) about 100 m east of the jetty [NG 946 069]. The rocks exposed on the foreshore in closure B consist of a grey micaceous semipelitic and gneissose psammite with quartzofeldspathic augen up to several centimetres across and streaks, lenses and pods of hornblendite and biotite-hornblende-gneiss up to 0.5 m across (Plate 1). These, together with numerous concordant quartzofeldspathic lenticles are isoclinally folded with limbs lying parallel to the dominant foliation. Similar rocks occur

by the roadside in closure A (Figure 6). The psammitic and semipelitic augen gneisses, but not the hornblendic rocks, are again seen on the east limb of fold closure C. The hornblendite is composed chiefly of interlocking crystals up to 1 cm long of hornblende with very minor biotite; the biotite-hornblende gneiss is composed, in addition, of essential oligoclase/andesine, K-feldspar and quartz, together with a little epidote (Tanner, 1971).

The status of the folds at the head of Loch Hourn is discussed elsewhere (p.44) where it is suggested that fold closures B and C, which fold the foliation in the pelite adjoining the Lewisian rocks are the closures of late folds ($D3_M$) in the Glenfinnan Division.

The Lewisian and associated Moine rocks in Glen Shiel are mainly disposed as bands trending NNE and dipping steeply ESE. At one locality on the south side of the valley [NH 004 131] hornblende-schist and interbanded psammite with concordant pegmatite veinlets are folded by $D1_M$ isoclinal minor folds which are in turn refolded by open to tight $D2_M$ minor folds (Plate 2).

**Plate 1**   Shore exposure at Kinloch Hourn showing Lewisian inlier of hornblende gneiss.
(D1240)

**Plate 2**  Folded Lewisian inlier of hornblende gneiss in Moine psammite. South slope of
Glen Shiel. (D867)

# FOUR

# Moine

## INTRODUCTION

Metamorphosed sediments collectively known as 'Moine' crop out over a large area of the Northern Highlands from the line of the Moine Thrust eastwards and southwards to the Great Glen Fault. Within this area numerous occurrences of gneisses correlated with the Lewisian of the Caledonian Foreland represent fragments of the crystalline basement upon which the Moine was deposited unconformably. Radiometric dating of meta-igneous bodies lying within the Moine in areas adjoining the Kintail district has indicated that at least some Moine sediments were deposited before 1020 Ma and have been affected by Precambrian as well as Caledonian tectonic and metamorphic events (Roberts et al., 1984 and references therein). Although a long time gap is implied by the radiometric age determinations between the Precambrian events at 750–1000 Ma and the Caledonian

event at 440–465 Ma, it is not at present known exactly what the effects of the earlier event were, and so it is not possible to put ages to the individual deformation episodes recognized. In the account which follows only relative ages of deformation are used.

The Moine has been divided into three major tectono-stratigraphic units (Johnstone et al., 1969) and two of these, the Morar and Glenfinnan divisions, are represented within the Kintail district. The two divisions are separated from each other by a major tectonic break known as the Sgurr Beag Slide, generally regarded as an early Caledonian structure (Powell et al., 1981).

A lithostratigraphical succession has been established for the Morar Division of the type area (Johnstone et al., 1969) but, because of a lack of marker horizons and the structural complexity arising from polyphase folding, the order of succession is imperfectly known in many other areas, including

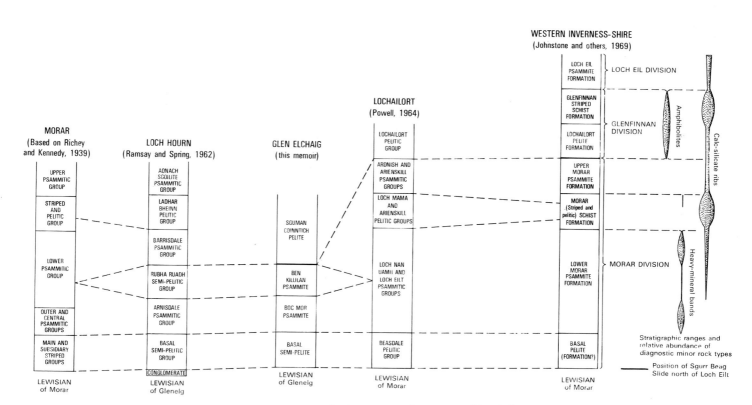

**Table 5**  Stratigraphical successions of the Moine rocks in western Inverness-shire (after Johnstone et al., 1969).

Kintail, and correlation from district to district is very difficult (Table 5). No satisfactory succession has been established for the Glenfinnan Division although, like the Morar Division, it appears to have a Lewisian basement. Because, on the mainland, the contact between the divisions is everywhere tectonic it has not been possible to determine their relative ages. However, on the island of Mull the Moine succession is unbroken and it has been suggested (Holdsworth et al., 1987) that the higher formations of the Morar Division are likely to be the lateral equivalent of formations of the Glenfinnan Division.

The rocks of both divisions were originally deposited as clastic sediments but subsequent metamorphism converted the sandstones into quartz-feldspar-granulites (psammites), and the siltstones and shales into quartz-mica-granulites (semipelites) and mica-schists (pelites). Wide outcrops of these three main rock types occur, as well as mixed assemblages in which the main lithologies are intimately interbanded. Pods and discontinuous bands of calcsilicate rock, most of which are probably metamorphosed calcareous concretions, occur in places but limestones are completely absent. The originally unconformable contact with the Lewisian has been much modified by deformation which has brought the banding in the Lewisian and the bedding in the Moine into parallelism.

The sequence of deformation events recognisable in the Moine, $D1_M - D4_M$, are not always simply related to those events recognised in the Lewisian, $D1_L - D6_L$, hence the use of subscript letters to refer to the effects in the first instance.

## AREA 2

The Moine north of the Strathconon Fault lying between the Sgurr Beag Slide and the major Lewisian outcrop north of Loch Duich consists of Morar Division rocks with sufficient sedimentary structures preserved to allow the order of deposition and a local stratigraphic succession to be established (Figure 7). In the west the rocks are the right way up with a general dip towards the ESE. However there are a number of tectonic breaks within this apparently continuous sequence which can be recognised by the presence of thin strips of Lewisian basement and repetitions of the lower part of the succession. The breaks are interpreted as ductile thrusts (slides) and are described in more detail later (p.26). In the east the structure is more complicated, with major

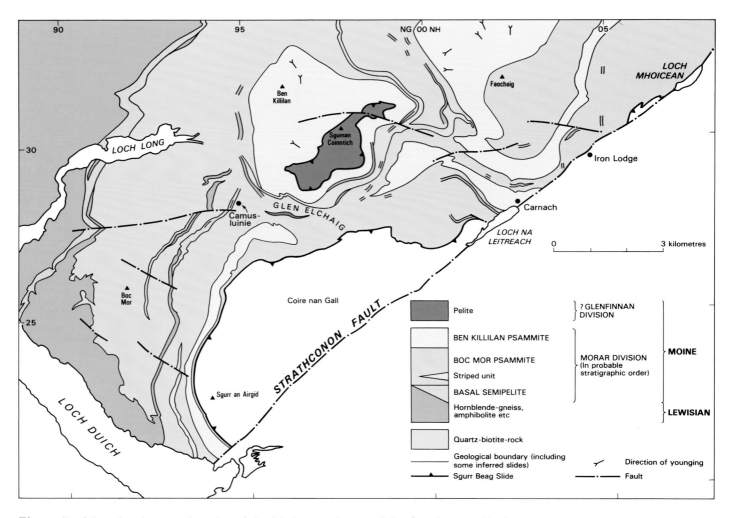

**Figure 7** Map showing stratigraphy of the Moine north-east of the Strathconon Fault.

folding as well as sliding controlling the distribution of out-crops. It is nevertheless still possible to recognise the formations established in the structurally simpler ground to the west.

## Stratigraphy and lithology

### THE BASAL SEMIPELITE

Semipelitic rocks form a nearly continuous envelope to the Lewisian rocks in the Morar and Knoydart areas where they are regarded as the lowest part of the Moine succession (Ramsay and Spring, 1962). Identical rocks in a similar structural position in Area 2 show evidence of extreme tectonic disruption and are blastomylonitic in part (p.30). Nevertheless the local occurrence of deformed conglomerate in the west Glenelg region (Sheet 71E; Clough 1901, Clough in Peach et al., 1910; Bailey and Tilley, 1952) and at Attadale (Sheet 82; Barber and May, 1975) supports the view that rocks at the base of the succession are preserved.

North of Loch Long the Basal Semipelite forms a band, about 150 m thick, lying above the Lewisian. South of Loch Long it diverges from the main Moine–Lewisian boundary and forms a narrow strip which separates the Western from the Eastern facies of the Lewisian. It is also found closely associated with the Lewisian at Camus-luinie [NG 948 286] where it has a maximum thickness of 120 m (Figure 7).

The Basal Semipelite typically consists of mica-schist containing scattered augen of white quartz and feldspar. A small amount of hornblende, occurring as disseminated grains and concentrated along some of the foliation surfaces, is commonly present. In places the schist has a very fine-grained mylonitic texture and consists of minute granules of quartz, feldspar, epidote and shreds of biotite, forming a foliated groundmass to larger crystals of feldspar which survive as lenticular relics. Abundant strongly folded concordant quartz veinlets project from weathered surfaces and are a characteristic feature which has been noted in other areas (Ramsay and Spring, 1962; Johnstone et al., 1969).

Psammitic bands, some thick enough to be shown on the 1:50 000 map, are common and a few contain grains of feldspar which, although somewhat granulitised, are still recognisably detrital. Small pebbles and sedimentary granules are particularly well seen in the shore section on the north side of Loch Long [NG 911 301]. Lenticles of hornblendic rocks ranging from mappable units down to laminae a few millimetres thick are found within the mica-schist. Rock types within the lenticles include hornblende-gneiss and amphibolite, both of typical Lewisian aspect.

The mylonitic texture of much of the mica-schist and the presence of Lewisian rocks, interpreted as tectonically incorporated lenticles, show that the Basal Semipelite has been subjected to extreme deformation, although the survival of sedimentary grains shows that the psammitic bands are only moderately deformed.

### THE BOC MOR PSAMMITE

In the Loch Long area and at Camus-luinie the Basal Semipelite is overlain by a psammite which is very well exposed on Boc Mor [NG 917 259]. The boundary is sharp and is exposed at a number of localities south west of Camus-

luinie. In the Loch Long area it is located at the base of a very prominent escarpment and is not exposed. South of the River Glennan the Basal Semipelite is absent and the Boc Mor Psammite rests directly on the Eastern Lewisian. West of Boc Mor [NG 901 262 to NG 907 262] the contact, which can be located to within 0.1 m, can be followed round a spectacular series of large eastward-plunging reclined folds (Barber et al., 1978). In general the Lewisian rocks are relatively poorly exposed in the neighbourhood of the contact, but can usually be found as closely foliated rock, splitting into hornblendic and biotite-rich layers, projecting as slabs from the grassy slopes, while the Moine rocks are perfectly exposed in small cliffs overlooking the contact. Wherever the actual boundary can be seen the foliation within the Lewisian and Moine rocks is parallel and concordant.

To the east of the contact the Boc Mor Psammite outcrop forms an extensive tract of elevated country between Loch Long and Loch Duich. In detail the topography is extremely rugged, being made up of barren rocky crags separated by peat bogs. In this area and in Glen Elchaig narrow bands and discontinuous lenses of Lewisian rocks lie along certain horizons, interpreted as slide zones (see p.29), within the Boc Mor Psammite. The sliding and several major folds have given rise to a complex outcrop pattern (Figure 7) but it seems probable that all the areas shown as Boc Mor Psammite are parts of a single lithostratigraphic formation.

The psammite, which is remarkably uniform in appearance, is a pale grey or pinkish-weathering muscovite-bearing quartzofeldspathic rock in which biotite is normally a very subordinate constituent. It contains abundant strongly rodded concordant quartz veins and in some of the slide zones quartzofeldspathic leucosomes give the rock a migmatitic structure. Grains of feldspar, mainly microcline and commonly still recognisable as being of detrital origin, are sufficiently abundant to show the arkosic affinities of the original sediment. The grains are normally up to 2 mm in diameter but small pebbles have also been found. Variations in texture and the presence of micaceous bands give the rock a layered structure which is very strongly folded in most exposures. No sedimentary structures have been found. A secondary flagginess, resulting from the parallelism of attenuated bedding and a pronounced schistosity, is seen within some of the slide zones. Black lenticular layers of heavy minerals up to a few centimetres thick are fairly common, for example south-west of Camus-luinie [NG 938 265]. They contain iron-oxide, epidote, sphene, zircon, garnet and apatite and are considered to represent placer concentrations in which all the minerals except zircon and sphene have been recrystallised. Calcsilicate pods, which are a characteristic feature of the upper part of the Morar Division (Johnstone et al., 1969), are absent in the Boc Mor Psammite.

Impersistent bands of pelite, typically up to 0.5 m thick, are present throughout the Boc Mor Psammite but only make up a small (less than 5 per cent) proportion of the total thickness. Pelitic bands, some more than 2 m thick, are unusually abundant on the western slopes of Gleann a'Choire Dhomhain [NG 99 32] and on the west side of Sgurr an Airgid there is a very distinctive striped unit, thinning towards the north, composed of semipelite, dark micaceous psammite and pelite, locally with garnet (Figure 7). In the steep slope above Loch Duich a stream follows the sharp contact at the base of the unit, which is here about 60 m thick. Although semipelite forms part of this striped unit it is generally absent from the Boc Mor Psammite.

The position of the Boc Mor Psammite in relation to the Basal Semipelite and the Lewisian, its general lithology and, in particular, the presence of heavy mineral bands and the absence of calcsilicate pods, leave no doubt that it is equivalent to the Arnisdale Psammite of Loch Hourn (Ramsay and Spring, 1962), ie the lower part of the Lower Psammite (Powell, 1974) (Table 5).

### THE BEN KILLILAN PSAMMITE

The junction between the Boc Mor Psammite and the Ben Killilan Psammite is in some places a slide zone and in others a sedimentary transition, typically about 20 m thick, in which pale-coloured arkosic psammite gives way to dark grey psammite with semipelitic bands. Lewisian slices do not occur within the Ben Killilan Psammite although they may lie along its margin where this is a slide zone, for example south-east of Sguman Coinntich [NG 98 29].

The psammite is a medium- to fine-grained rock, grey in colour on freshly broken surfaces due to the presence of disseminated biotite, and made up of bands and stripes showing all gradations between psammite and semipelite. The semipelitic bands, up to 1.0 m thick, are garnetiferous and form up to 40 per cent of the sequence. At a few localities a schistosity is deflected around microcline porphyroblasts containing numerous inclusions which are finer grained than the matrix in which the porphyroblasts lie. Relict detrital clasts are only rarely recognisable. Cross-bedding has been recorded at a number of localities on Ben Killilan and north-west of Faochaig (Figure 7). These are areas where the Ben Killilan Psammite is very thick; elsewhere there has probably been tectonic thinning and consequent destruction of sedimentary structures. Segregated quartzofeldspathic material is generally scarce except on the south-east side of Sguman Coinntich where the rock is coarse grained and gneissose. The psammite contains a few calcsilicate ribs and these are particularly common on the west side of Faochaig where they are made up of quartz, plagioclase, garnet, epidote, zoisite, muscovite and sphene.

On Ben Killilan and on the east side of Gleann a'Choire Dhomhain cross-bedding and a sedimentary transition indicate a passage from an older Boc Mor Psammite into a younger Ben Killilan Psammite and this evidence is the basis of the proposed stratigraphical succession. Correlation of the Ben Killilan Psammite with the Morar – Loch Hourn succession is uncertain because of the lack of continuity of outcrop. However, the upward passage from rocks confidently correlated with the Arnisdale Psammite and lithological similarity indicate that the Ben Killilan Psammite is probably the equivalent of the Rubha Ruadh Semipelite (Ramsay and Spring, 1962) i.e. the semipelite within the Lower Psammite (Powell, 1974), although the rocks are somewhat more quartzose in the Kintail district.

### THE SGUMAN COINNTICH PELITE

The Sguman Coinntich Pelite is separated from the adjoining Ben Killilan Psammite by a sharp contact which may be a major tectonic break, although no Lewisian rocks or other evidence to suggest the presence of a slide has been found either along the contact or within the pelite. An impersistent band of pelitic gneiss up to 50 m thick south-east of Camus-luinie [NG 961 279] may be a tectonically detached portion of the Sguman Coinntich Pelite (Figure 7).

The pelite is a massive, coarse-grained garnetiferous rock with abundant quartzofeldspathic leucosomes. It contains a few thin bands of psammite and semipelite and rare pods of calcsilicate rock and garnetiferous amphibolite. The latter is not accompanied by typical Lewisian rocks, for example hornblende-gneiss, and is probably a Moine metasediment or a metamorphosed basic igneous rock intrusive into the Moine.

The Sguman Cointich Pelite is likely to be a structurally isolated portion of either the Morar Pelite (Morar Division) or the Lochailort Pelite (Glenfinnan Division) which are the only major pelites within the Moine of Western Inverness-shire (Johnstone et al., 1969, Powell, 1974). The strongly migmatitic condition of the Sguman Coinntich Pelite and the presence of amphibolite pods suggests correlation with the Lochailort Pelite and if this is the case then the boundary of the pelite is probably the Sgurr Beag Slide (p.46). There is, however, no direct evidence for the presence of a slide at the boundary of the pelite although the adjacent Ben Killilan Psammite shows evidence of increasing flagginess as the contact is approached. Present available information leads to the conclusion the pelite should be assigned to the Glenfinnan Division.

## Structure

### SUMMARY OF MAIN STRUCTURAL FEATURES

The main structural features of Area 2 can be conveniently described from west to east. West of Boc Mor folding of the Moine – Lewisian contact provides evidence of the earliest recognisable deformation event affecting the Moine (Figure 8). Here a major isoclinal synform ($D1_M$) is refolded by ESE-plunging reclined folds ($D2_M$). Further east, stratigraphic repetitions attributable to major $D1_M$ isoclinal folding appear to be absent and the $D2_M$ deformation was so intense that almost all $D1_M$ minor structures have been obliterated.

Between Boc Mor and Camus-luinie the foliation has a general easterly dip which is remarkably constant, although on a small scale there is much tight folding ($D2_M$) with a very prominent axial rodding and mineral lineation. Repetitions of the sequence Lewisian Gneiss – Basal Semipelite – Boc Mor Psammite reveal the presence of two major slides (ductile thrusts) lying concordant with the general attitude of the foliation. $D2_M$ fabrics are strongly developed in rocks within the slide zones and evidence will be presented suggesting that the slides are, at least in part, $D2_M$ structures.

In the area lying between Camus-luinie and the north-east corner of Sheet 72W major $D3_M$ folds distort earlier structures including a number of important slide zones. The largest $D3_M$ structures are the Sguman Coinntich and Faochaig folds. The former appears to be synformal with a strongly curvilinear hinge and resembles the recently described Glen Dessary Synform (Roberts et al., 1984) which has a strongly curved hinge and sheath-like geometry. Erosion of the Sguman Coinntich fold has given rise to a ring-shaped outcrop of the Ben Killilan Psammite (Figure 7). The Faochaig fold is a south-east-plunging sideways-closing structure north of Carnach (Figure 7). However, the fold extends beyond the northern limit of Sheet 72W and the shape of the complete structure is unknown. The highly complex outcrop pattern throughout the area between Camus-luinie and the north-east corner of Sheet 72W is partly due to the branching character of the slide zones (Figure 11) and partly to the sheath-like geometry of the D3 folds. However, the structure is not sufficiently well understood to enable reliable cross-sections to be drawn.

## D1$_M$ STRUCTURES

Folds formed during the earliest recognisable period of deformation to affect the Moine are well displayed in the Boc Mor Psammite close to the outcrop of the Eastern Lewisian. Further east these early structures are only rarely distinguishable from the pervasive folds and fabrics formed during D2$_M$ deformation.

Large-scale D1$_M$ and D2$_M$ folds can be seen affecting the boundary between the Lewisian and Moine where it extends along the southern flank of Carn Glas [908 263] and in the area to the south (Figure 8). A careful inspection of almost any exposure of Moine psammite in this area will show that it is complexly folded on a small scale by large numbers of long-limbed isoclines. These isoclines (D1$_M$) are commonly seen to be refolded by more open types of folds (D2$_M$). Pelitic layers interbanded with broadly folded psammitic layers are thrown into complex puckers so that while the early isoclines are preserved in the psammites they are not seen in the pelites. A dominant foliation is seen to have an axial-plane relationship to the D1$_M$ isoclinal folds which affect the mineral banding. Petrographic evidence (Barber, 1968) suggests that after the formation of the isoclines and its corresponding axial-plane structure the rock recrystallised producing a granulitic texture.

North-east-plunging rodding structures clearly related to early isoclinal folds have been recorded at a few localities in the Boc Mor Psammite near its junction with the Eastern Lewisian. The rods are crossed by a dominant mineral elongation lineation (D2$_M$). They lie within the plane of foliation and may undulate within this plane indicating that they have been subjected to a later deformation. Where the rods and associated isoclines have been reorientated into an ESE direction and are no longer crossed at an angle by the ESE lineation (D2$_M$) they are not distinguishable from structures formed during the later phase of folding.

The salient of Moine psammite which projects into the area of Lewisian outcrop at Loch na Faolaig is interpreted as a D1$_M$ isoclinal fold core refolded during D2$_M$ (Figure 8). The Moine rocks and the adjacent Lewisian show intense small-scale isoclinal folding in this region, and the foliation in both rock groups is essentially parallel in the neighbourhood of their contact. When traced south-westwards from Loch na Faolaig the outcrop of the Moine psammite narrows from a width of 100 m to only 2 m where it is last seen. Clearly on a large scale the boundary between the Lewisian and Moine rocks must cut across the axial plane foliation of the isoclinal folds and it is for this reason that the psammite is considered to lie in large-scale isoclinal fold core of the same generation.

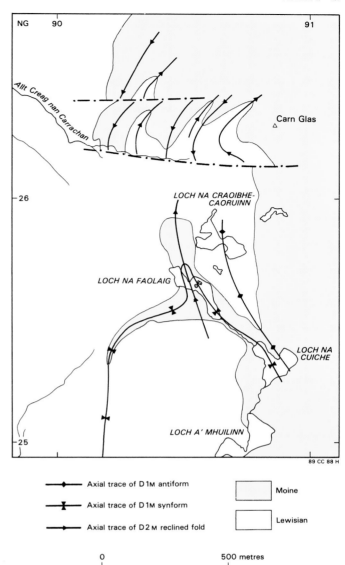

**Figure 8**   Folded Moine – Lewisian boundary west of Boc Mor.

## D2$_M$ STRUCTURES

The Moine of Area 2 underwent strong penetrative deformation during D2$_M$ and the associated minor structures are abundant everywhere. In the west, around Carn Glas and Loch na Faolaig, where earlier structures are preserved (Figure 8), D2$_M$ folds deform D1$_M$ structures and in the east they are refolded by major D3$_M$ folds.

Barber (1968) has shown that the D1$_M$ folding was followed by recrystallisation in the amphibolite facies. A second period of deformation followed the recrystallisation of the Boc Mor Psammite as muscovite crystals, developed during recrystallisation, are bent, show undulose extinction and are enclosed in augen structures. This deformation was also responsible for the bending of plagioclase twin lamellae, shredding of biotite flakes and the enclosure of garnet crystals in augen. It also led to the development of the planar fabric, seen in some sections of psammite, characterised by highly elongated stringers of quartz with sutured contacts, undulose extinction and a high degree of preferred lattice orientation. It was also responsible for the dominant linear structure seen in the same specimens.

Large-scale $D2_M$ folds which affect the boundary between the Moine and Lewisian rocks in the neighbourhood of Carn Glas (Figure 8) have ESE-plunging axes. The adjacent Moine rocks in the axial regions of these major folds contain large numbers of minor folds of open type whose axes plunge in the same direction and whose axial planes also dip in an easterly direction. Folds of this type, where the fold axes plunge down the dip of the axial planes, have been termed 'reclined' by Fleuty (1964). Although in most exposures the minor $D2_M$ folds appear to be simple structures with a re-clined geometry close examination commonly reveals eyed-structures in sections normal to the ESE plunge. Barber (1968) interpreted these as the product of fold interference (Ramsay, 1967). However, more recently it has been shown that under high-strain folds with extremely curved hinges, commonly known as sheath folds, can be formed during a single phase of progressive deformation (Cobbold and Quin-quis, 1980) and it seems probable that many of the eyed-structures in the Boc Mor Psammite are of this type.

The minor reclined folds possess an axial-plane cleavage which forms the dominant planar fabric of the Moine. In the limbs of the folds it lies subparallel to the mineral layering, forming a composite foliation which, in the west of the area, dips uniformly to the ESE (Figure 9). In the east its attitude is very variable due to later refolding.

The $D2_M$ linear structure in the Moine is an elongation of minerals and mineral aggregates on the foliation surfaces. Rodded quartz veins, striated and grooved parallel to their lengths are also common, especially in more micaceous bands. Psammitic bands locally show incipient boudinage, pinching and swelling, especially where they are enclosed in more micaceous bands. Concordant pegmatite veins are commonly drawn out into a series of augen-shaped blebs along the foliation surfaces. The quartz of these veins is striated and the feldspars, often with an augen-shaped form, are elongated in the direction of dip of the foliation planes to form a linear structure.

In the west the plunge of $D2_M$ lineations is uniformly towards the ESE (Figure 10). Further east, in an area of coaxial refolding to be described later, SE and SSE plunges predominate.

Important slide zones, which were probably active during $D2_M$ also occur in Area 2, and are described below.

## $D3_M$ STRUCTURES

In the western part of Area 2 the limbs and axial plane schistosity of D2 folds together give rise to a uniformly dipping foliation. Towards the east this relatively simple structure gives way to a very complex system of major folds which distort the earlier $D2_M$ structures (Figure 9).

This complex area has been subdivided into a number of smaller units (Figure 9, A to K) and foliation measurements within each have been plotted stereographically in order to determine the axial orientation of the major folds. The poles to foliation planes lie on girdles and show that all the fold

hinges plunge towards the south-east quadrant at between 28° and 54°. The axial planes of the folds are ill defined and appear to be very variable in orientation.

The axial trace of fold I (Figure 9) has only been followed for about 600 m WNW from the closure of the Ben Killilan Psammite. Beyond this point it is unrecognisable but is almost certainly refolded by fold H. It is therefore probable that I is a $D2_M$ fold and H a $D3_M$ fold. Both structures are almost coaxial, the difference in plunge being only about 10°.

All the remaining major folds in the eastern part of Area 2 refold minor intrafolial folds of $D2_M$ age so that the $D2_M$ axial traces swing round with changes in the trend of folia-tion defining the later ($D3_M$) major folds. Minor $D3_M$ folds are open in style with a locally developed axial planar crenulation cleavage. A penetrative axial-planar schistosity is generally absent in both quartzofeldspathic and micaceous lithologies. Despite the refolding of $D2_M$ planar structures the plunge of the $D2_M$ fold hinges and the $D2_M$ quartz rod-ding remains remarkably constant towards the SE quadrant (Figure 10). This consistency is the result of $D2_M$ and $D3_M$ being approximately coaxial throughout the area.

The distribution of outcrops is largely controlled by two major $D3_M$ folds. The ring-shaped outcrop of Ben Killilan Psammite (Figure 9, B, F, E) is the result of erosion of the major Sguman Coinntich Fold. Foliation measurements sug-gest that it is a tight synformal sheath fold plunging at 30° towards the SE. The Sguman Coinntich Pelite is probably a klippe of Glenfinnan Division rocks separated from the sur-rounding Morar Division rocks by a downfold of the Sgurr Beag Slide. The $D3_M$ Faochaig Fold (Figure 9, A, C) is reclined, closing towards the SW and extending NE into Sheet 82 beyond the area of the present survey. It is an open structure in the SW becoming isoclinal towards the NE. In the ground between the Faochaig and Sguman Coinntich folds, branching, pre-$D3_M$, slide zones (see p.32) can be followed round large open $D3_M$ folds (Figure 9, G, J, K).

The sideways-closing form of the $D3_M$ folds and uncer-tainties regarding the nature of pre-$D3_M$ slides make the con-struction of cross-sections across the eastern part of Area 2 highly speculative and further research is required to fully elucidate the structures.

## TECTONIC SLIDE ZONES

Several major folds occur in Area 2 but folding alone cannot adequately account for the distribution of Lewisian inliers or the various formations of the Moine succession and it is evi-dent that the present structure was formed by a complex pro-cess of tectonic sliding (ductile thrusting) as well as folding. The importance of slides in the Moine is now generally accepted (Powell, 1974). Most have been located mainly on stratigraphic evidence but structural effects, notably the development of flagginess, have been described (Rathbone and Harris, 1979, Langford, 1980) and these provide addi-tional criteria for their recognition.

In Area 2 the symmetrical arrangement of Moine rocks with respect to each inlier that would be expected if the Lewi-sian occupied isoclinal fold cores does not occur. Instead the succession is broken and parts of the sequence Lewisian Gneiss – Basal Semipelite – Boc Mor Psammite – Ben Killilan Psammite are repeated. The inliers lie along certain

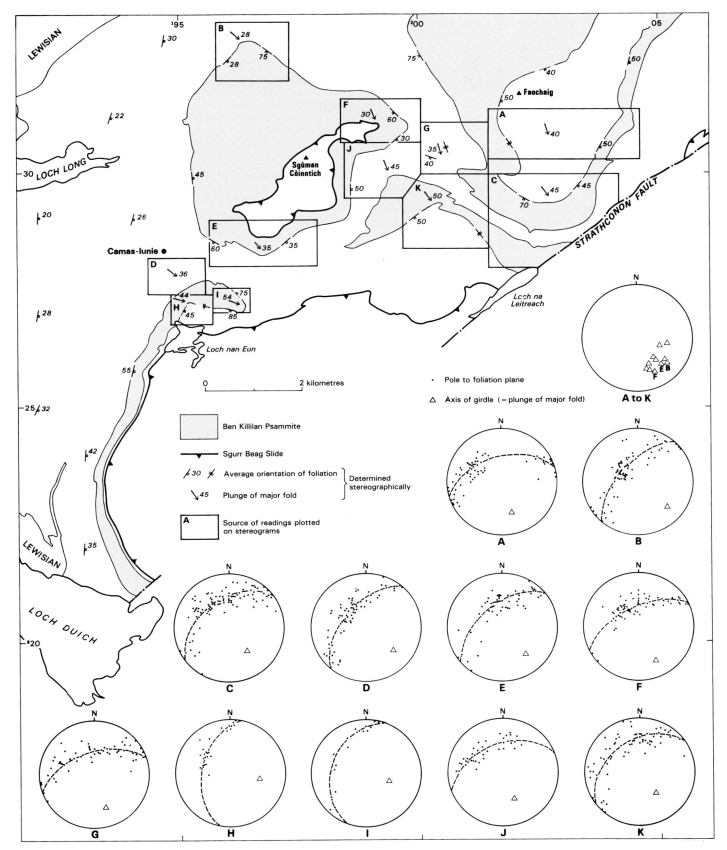

**Figure 9**   Map of Area 2 showing average orientation of banding and plunge of minor folds.

**Figure 10** Map of Areas 2 and 3 showing plunge of mineral lineation and rodding.

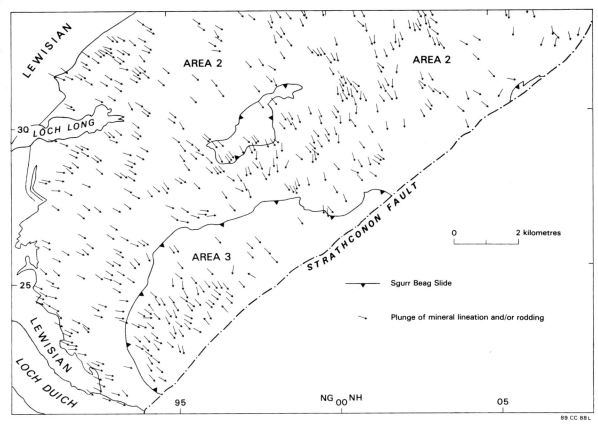

89 CC 88 L

horizons, commonly containing flaggy and platy rocks, which are taken to indicate a high state of strain associated with sliding. The movements appear to have affected large volumes of rock and in most cases it is necessary to distinguish slide zones many metres thick rather than single planes of movement (Figure 11). On a local scale the slide zones are concordant with respect to the dominant foliation and in the east they are folded with it. Some have branching outcrops, indicating a complex structure which is not yet fully understood.

Zones 1, 2, 4, 5, 9, 11, 13 and 14 (Figure 11) are characterised by the presence of Lewisian slices and a flaggy structure in the adjoining Moine. The remainder possess additional features notably the presence of migmatitic psammite and the very distinctive quartz-biotite-rock. These rock types are intimately interbanded with each other, and commonly enclose Lewisian slices. The quartz-biotite-rock cannot be matched lithologically with any 'normal' Moine or Lewisian rock and appears to be confined to the horizons identified as slide zones.

The quartz-biotite-rock owes its distinctive appearance partly to its mineralogy and partly to its strongly developed $D2_M$ linear fabric. As the name implies the rock is composed of quartz and biotite, the latter ranging from 1 to 20 per cent and averaging approximately 10 per cent. Zircon, iron oxide, sphene, muscovite and apatite are normally present as accessory minerals. Epidote has only been found in a few examples and feldspars are either absent or present only in very small amounts. The quartz occurs as irregularly shaped or somewhat elongated grains of variable size up to about

2.0 mm across (Figure 12). The elongated grains show some preferred dimensional orientation and measurements with a universal stage indicate that all the grains have a strong preferred lattice orientation. Slight undulose extinction is sometimes seen but it is evident that the quartz has been almost completely annealed. Biotite is disseminated throughout the rock as isolated crystals and crystal groups which have a very characteristic spindle shape (Figure 12). Mutually perpendicular sections show that the spindles are commonly about 2.50 mm by 1.00 mm by 0.25 mm with the longest dimension showing an almost perfect preferred orientation which gives the rock its penetrative lineaton. Sections normal to the lineation show some preferred orientation of the basal cleavage and demonstrate that there is a weak planar component to the fabric. On freshly broken surfaces the black spindle-shaped biotite crystals in a matrix of glassy quartz impart a distinctive character to the rock which enable it, even on the smallest scale, to be readily recognisable in the field or in hand specimen. Weathered surfaces are pitted due to the disintegration and removal of the biotite. Variations in the proportion of biotite give rise to a weakly developed compositional layering which is locally folded ($D2_M$).

The quartz-biotite-rock occurrences vary from narrow impersistent bands, which are too small to be mapped individually, to units tens of metres thick which extend for kilometres along strike. It is normally found in contact with migmatitic rocks derived from the Boc Mor Psammite and this extremely close and consistent spatial association suggests a genetic relationship between migmatisation and the

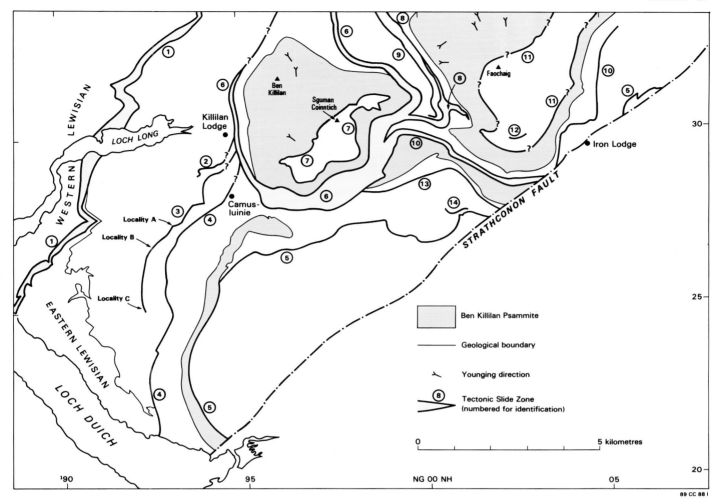

**Figure 11**   Map of Area 2 showing tectonic slide zones.

development of quartz-biotite-rock. Sharp and gradational contacts occur, the latter being marked by the presence of thin layers of psammite and coarsely crystalline quartzo-feldspathic leucosomes within the quartz-biotite-rock. The transition is also marked by a structural change from a predominantly linear fabric to a predominantly planar one. The contacts are normally concordant with the layering in the psammite but a few cross-cutting examples have been found.

The migmatitic psammite associated with the quartz-biotite-rock contains a very variable proportion (up to 75 per cent) of leucosomes composed of microcline, oligoclase and quartz. Thicknesses range from a few millimetres to several centimetres and thicker concordant pegmatite sheets show-ing boudinage structure also occur. They have sharp or dif-fuse boundaries with the metasedimentary host which varies from a normal textured psammite to an exceedingly coarse-grained rock, almost granitic in aspect. The leucosomes are commonly folded ($D2_M$) and thin sections of migmatitic psammite from zone 3 (Figure 11) show that some of the large feldspars forming the leucosomes have been broken and pulled apart in the direction of the $D2_M$ planar fabric. Gaps between the fragments are infilled with coarsely

crystalline quartz. The folds and the extended feldspars show that migmatisation was syn- or pre-tectonic with respect to $D2_M$.

DETAILS OF INDIVIDUAL SLIDE ZONES

North of Loch Long zone 1 (Figure 11) follows the Basal Semipelite and separates the Western Lewisian below from the Boc Mor Psammite above. It contains some psammitic bands and lenticular masses of Lewisian gneiss. The semi-pelitic rocks are very fine grained and composed of shreds of biotite, granules of quartz and epidote and lens-shaped por-phyroclasts of feldspar. Granulated relics of hornblende crystals also occur locally. A thick band of psammite within the slide zone at Sallachy [NG 910 300] is much less de-formed than the semipelite and still contains recognisable sedimentary grains. Most of the movement was taken up by the less competent micaceous lithology which acquired a blastomylonitic texture.

As it is traced southwards from Loch Long zone 1 passes into the main Glenelg–Attadale inlier where it separates the Western from the Eastern facies of the Lewisian. This part of the zone has been studied in detail by Barber (1968) and is important because of the evidence it provides on the timing

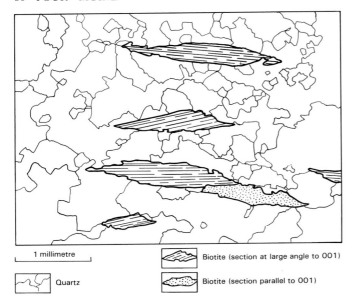

1 millimetre

Quartz

Biotite (section at large angle to 001)

Biotite (section parallel to 001)

**Figure 12**  Drawing of a thin section of quartz-biotite rock cut parallel to lineation.

of sliding relative to the fold history of the area. It is made up of augen mica-schist, quartzofeldspathic mica-schist, Lewisian gneiss and Moine psammite. Although the augen mica-schist is partly derived from the Basal Semipelite it probably contains a greater admixture of Lewisian material than the semipelite north of Loch Long. Amphibolite, hornblendite and migmatitic acid gneiss, all of Western Lewisian type, occur as lenticles, varying from mappable units within the mica-schists down to the scale of a thin section. The larger lenticles contain rods which plunge in an ENE direction. The rods are evidently relict structures, probably of D1 age, surviving in relatively undeformed masses of Western Lewisian rock which were incorporated in zone 1 during sliding.

The mica-schist surrounding the lenticles contains quartz veins which are isoclinally folded (D2$_M$). Mineral banding is not commonly developed but where it occurs it is also folded into long-limbed isoclines. The dominant foliation, which has a general dip of about 35° towards the ESE, is parallel to the axial planes of the isoclines. A very well-developed ESE-plunging mineral lineation is orientated parallel to the axes of the isoclinal folds as are quartz rods formed by the thickening of veins in the region of fold closures.

In thin section the D2$_M$ foliation in the groundmass of the mica-schist is seen to sweep round lenticles of granoblastic rock to form augen structures. The augen, from aggregates to individual crystals, appear to be relics of the original rocks from which the mica-schist was derived. Hornblende, biotite, muscovite, epidote and small garnets forming the groundmass are recrystallised. The mineral assemblage indicates that the recrystallisation took place under amphibolite facies conditions of metamorphism and because some of the crystals cut across the foliation the recrystallisation was, at least in part, later than the formation of the foliation.

The recrystallised minerals which define the foliation are broken and disrupted by concordant shear planes and every gradation can be seen in thin section from a foliated rock cut

by a few shear planes, to a rock which has been completely mylonitised. There was no retrograde metamorphism associated with this granulation, all the minerals apparently remaining stable.

At many localities a crenulation cleavage, dipping towards the north-east, cuts the foliation and the shear planes at a high angle. The cleavage is seen in the field as kinking of the mica flakes, and in thin section by the granulation of minerals lying along the cleavage planes.

To summarise, slide zone 1 was evidently initiated during D2$_M$ and acted as a movement horizon between a relatively undeformed, resistant block of Western Lewisian gneisses and the highly deformed Eastern Lewisian and Moine rocks which overlie it. The main movement led to the formation of a penetrative foliation and was accompanied by recrystallisation (amphibolite facies) which probably continued after the movement had ceased. Renewed granulitisation along closely spaced shear planes produced, in places, mylonite which predates the development of a crenulation cleavage which may be of D3$_M$ age.

Slide zone 2 is marked by a band of Lewisian gneiss which, at NG 9389 2889, is about 3 m thick. Here a sharp contact separates the Lewisian gneiss from normal psammite below. The upper boundary is not exposed. It dies out rapidly in a southerly direction and probably merges with zone 6 towards the north-east (Figure 11).

Slide zone 3 is up to 50 m thick and crops out in the lower part of an escarpment formed of massive Boc Mor Psammite. The relationships of the various lithological components, which are well displayed in a number of sections, provide important evidence relevant to the interpretation of the large-scale structure of the area. In general the slide zone consists of flaggy hornblendic gneiss (Lewisian) overlying migmatitic psammite containing discontinuous bands of quartz-biotite-rock but in detail (Figure 13) the structure is found to be more complicated. For example at locality A the Lewisian occurs as two leaves separated by a band of migmatitic psammite with ribs of quartz-biotite-rock. The upper leaf is overlain by 4 m of the Basal Semipelite which is in turn overlain by the Boc Mor Psammite. This part of the sequence is in its original stratigraphic order and is interpreted as the base of a major overthrust nappe. The migmatitic leucosomes and ribs of quartz-biotite-rock in the underlying psammite die out downwards and both therefore appear to be genetically related to the slide.

At locality B (Figures 11, 13) two Lewisian bands are present but the Basal Semipelite is absent. Hornblendic gneiss debris shows that the Lewisian persists southwards for a further 500 m or so but at locality C it is missing and the slide zone is represented entirely by rocks derived from the Boc Mor Psammite. Here weakly migmatised psammite with bands of quartz-biotite-rock is overlain by a flaggy horizon consisting of interbanded psammite, micaceous psammite and a few thin pelitic stripes. The migmatitic psammite, quartz-biotite-rock and flaggy horizon die out a short distance south of locality C and the slide zone cannot be traced any further.

Slide zone 4 runs parallel to zone 3 and lies approximately 500 m above it. However, the absence of migmatitic psammite and quartz-biotite-rock and the greater development of flagginess in the underlying and overlying psammite are im-

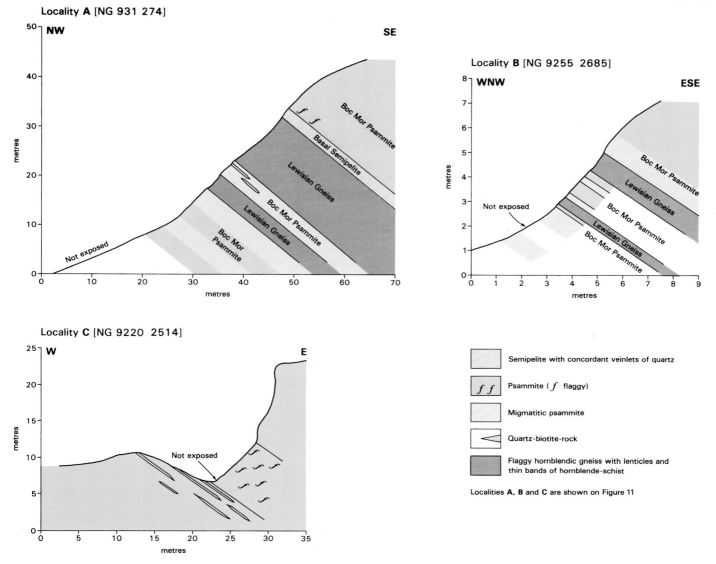

Locality **A** [NG 931 274]

Locality **B** [NG 9255 2685]

Locality **C** [NG 9220 2514]

Semipelite with concordant veinlets of quartz

*f f*  Psammite ( *f* flaggy)

Migmatitic psammite

Quartz-biotite-rock

Flaggy hornblendic gneiss with lenticles and thin bands of hornblende-schist

Localities **A**, **B** and **C** are shown on Figure 11

**Figure 13**   Cross-sections through slide zone 3.

portant points of contrast. Zone 4 has the form of a sheet, dipping at between 35° and 40° to ESE, which can be traced continuously for a distance of 7 km. In the south it follows the margin of the Glenelg – Attadale Lewisian inlier, while in the north, it probably merges with, or is cut by, zone 6 but the critical evidence for this is hidden beneath the alluvium of the River Elchaig. The zone of highly strained rocks includes the Basal Semipelite, up to 130 m thick but dying out completely towards the south. The semipelite contains numerous lenticular masses of Lewisian gneiss and on its western side a more continuous band, an arrangement which is taken to indicate that the succession; Lewisian basement – Basal Semipelite – Boc Mor Psammite has been thrust over Boc Mor Psammite. Flagginess extends downwards from the Lewisian gneiss for about 25 m into the underlying psammite. Above, about 170 m of the Boc Mor Psammite is in a flaggy condition and between Camus-luinie and An Leth Allt the outcrop of these flaggy rocks is marked

by an erosion hollow which has been partially infilled with glacial drift. Thin sections show that a $D2_M$ planar fabric is exceptionally well developed in the flaggy rocks.

Slide zone 5, which is taken as the boundary between Areas 2 and 3 (Figures 3, 11), separates Morar Division rocks from an overlying pelite which probably belongs to the Glenfinnan Division. The recognition of Glenfinnan Division rocks in Area 3 and correlation across the Strathconon Fault (p.60) suggests that zone 5 is an extension of the Sgurr Beag Slide. The outcrop of the Boc Mor Psammite at Camus-luinie can be traced around the major D2 fold closure in sub-Area 2 (Figure 9I) and then southwards where it becomes extremely thinned and flaggy in the slide zone. Zone 5 almost coincides with the 'Kintail Thrust' postulated by Clifford (1957). However, Clifford considered that the major break occurred at the top of the pelite, a conclusion which is not in accord with the new stratigraphic evidence, although the pelite is undoubtedly in a highly strained condition in the upper part of a slide zone.

Slide zone 6 is a major and complex structure which contains the thickest and most continuous developments of quartz-biotite-rock in the area as well as numerous small slices of Lewisian gneiss. To the north-east of Ben Killilan it is represented by a broad steeply inclined belt of variable migmatisation in the Boc Mor Psammite containing numerous bands of quartz-biotite-rock. As the zone is traced towards the south-east it approaches and then runs along the boundary of the Ben Killilan Psammite, providing clear evidence of the large-scale transgressive nature of the zone (Figure 11). $D3_M$ folding causes the outcrop to swing round to the south-west and it is in this area that mapping has shown that the slide zone, here composed principally of quartz-biotite-rock, is branched (Figure 11, zones 8 and 10). South-east of Sguman Coinntich, zone 6, here estimated to about 400 m thick, has a narrow but fairly continuous band of Lewisian gneiss along its north-west margin. The remainder is made up of interbanded quartz-biotite-rock and migmatitic psammite, the proportion of quartz-biotite-rock decreasing towards the south-east. Small Lewisian slices and a few thin bands of coarse garnetiferous pelite are also found throughout the zone in this area. In Glen Elchaig the outcrop swings round towards the north. On the south side of the glen [NG 961 279] it contains a band of migmatitic pelite, 30 to 50 m thick. As it is traced towards the north zone 6 thins and diverges from the boundary of the Ben Killilan Psammite. In the woods south of Killilan Lodge rocks of unusual appearance have been produced by soda metasomatism of Lewisian gneiss and migmatitic psammite (see p.59). The stream section [NG 949 303] near the lodge provides an accessible section through the zone which is here represented by about 100 m of interbanded Lewisian gneiss, psammite (migmatitic in part), quartz-biotite-rock and garnetiferous pelite. The zone can be traced northwards with confidence for a further 1.3 km where, in the Boglie Burn [NG 9499 3165], it consists of 1.0 m of migmatitic psammite resting on 0.5 m of Lewisian hornblende-gneiss. Beyond the Boglie Burn the line is conjectural although there is a small exposure of quartz-biotite-rock at [NG 9607 3282].

The Morar Division is regionally overlain by the Glenfinnan Division, the junction between the two being marked by the Sgurr Beag Slide. The correlation of the Sguman Coinntich Pelite with Glenfinnan Division rocks therefore implies that the pelite is an tectonic outlier of the Glenfinnan Division separated from the surrounding Morar Division rocks by the Sgurr Beag Slide (slide zone 7). The pelite with its bounding slide is folded into a major synform which is comparable with the Glenshian Synform in the Loch Eilt region of Inverness-shire (Powell et al., 1981; Baird, 1982). Erosion of the synform, which has an extremely curvilinear hinge, has given rise to the ring-shape outcrop of the slide. The structural effects of sliding are seen in the adjoining Ben Killilan Psammite which becomes increasingly flaggy as the boundary with the pelite is approached. A sliver of quartz-biotite-rock, 1.0 m thick, which runs along the boundary east of Sguman Coinntich [NG 9911 3095] appears to be an unusual and solitary occurrence in zone 7.

Slide zone 8 is a branch of zone 6 running east and then north to the summit of Sron na Gaoithe where a folded

($D3_M$) mass of quartz-biotite-rock, tapering out to the north and east, is very well exposed. A band of Lewisian gneiss on the east side of the quartz-biotite-rock continues north and is well exposed in Allt Gleann a'Choire Dhomhain. This strike section is of interest because bands of Lewisian gneiss are seen to bifurcate, the intervening wedges consisting of Moine psammite. This phenomenon is particularly well displayed at [NG 004 316] and suggests an anastomosing slide complex rather than a single dislocation.

Slide zone 9 crops out a short distance to the west of zone 8 and is marked by the presence of Lewisian slices in the Boc Mor Psammite.

Slide zone 10 appears to be a branch of zone 6 and in the west its position is marked by a number of small Lewisian slices, migmatitic psammite and a few bands of quartz-biotite-rock. The migmatitic psammite and associated quartz-biotite-rock die out towards the east, and north of Iron Lodge Lewisian bands are the only indications of its course.

The Ben Killilan Psammite north-west of Faochaig youngs to the south-east towards a psammite which is correlated with the Boc Mor Psammite. If this correlation is correct then the two psammites must be separated by a tectonic break (Figure 11, slide zone 11), although none of the usual features associated with sliding have been recorded at the boundary. A group of isolated lens-shaped bodies of hornblende-schist and a single exposure of quartz-biotite-rock indicates the presence of a slide at some distance from the boundary (zone 12).

Slide zone 13 appears to be a branch of zone 6 and can be traced as an almost continuous band of Lewisian hornblendic gneiss which has sharp contacts with the adjoining psammite.

Slide zone 14 is recognised by the presence of a narrow well-defined band of Lewisian gneiss broken and displaced by faults.

## METAMORPHIC AND STRUCTURAL HISTORY

The history of Area 2 is summarised in Table 6. $D1_M$ structures are only preserved in the west where a large isoclinal fold of the Moine–Lewisian boundary is refolded by a $D2_M$ reclined fold. Further east the effects of this early phase of deformation are uncertain; no major $D1_M$ isoclinal folds have been detected but in Area 3 interleaving of the Moine and Lewisian, probably by isoclinal folding, may have occurred at this stage (see p.33). The entire area was affected by penetrative deformation during $D2_M$ and large displacements along ductile thrusts (slides) are indicated by repetitions of the stratigraphic succession above zones showing evidence of high strain. In slide zone 1 there is good evidence that thrusting was initiated during D2. The remaining zones show evidence of movement during $D2_M$ but it is possible that some are older structures which were reactivated during $D2_M$. The presence of migmatite plus quartz-biotite-rock in some of the slide zones but not in others is of considerable interest. The rate of movement in each zone may have been important. If sliding was fast enough frictional heating may have contributed to migmatisation as suggested by Barr (1985, p.251). Barr also shows that a restite enriched in quartz and mica and strongly depleted in feldspar could be derived by the partial melting of psammite.

**Table 6** Sequence of events in the Moine of Area 2 and correlations with the sequence in the Western and Eastern Lewisian (Tables 1 and 4).

| | |
|---|---|
| D3$_M$ Major SE-plunging folding dying out towards the west | D5$_L$ |
| D2$_M$ Reclined folding with ESE- to SE-trending mineral lineation and rodding. Major sliding and stacking of thrust sheets. Development of flaggy zones and, in the west, mylonite. Migmatisation of the Boc Mor Psammite and the formation of quartz-biotite-rock in some, but not all, of the slide zones. Syn- to post-tectonic amphibolite facies metamorphism | D4$_L$ |
| D1$_M$ Isoclinal folding, mainly on a small scale, with axial plane schistosity and rodding lineation. Syn- to post-tectonic amphibolite facies metamorphism | D1$_L$ |
| Sedimentation of the Moine on the Lewisian basement | |

Fold episodes D2$_L$ and D3$_L$ in the Lewisian have not been recognised in the Moine

A restite origin for the quartz-biotite-rock is therefore a possibility which should be investigated. Tight reclined D2$_M$ folds with an associated mineral lineation occur throughout Area 2 and extend into the Eastern Lewisian (D4$_L$ in the Lewisian structural sequence). Slide zone 1 forms the boundary between Eastern Lewisian and Moine rocks which were highly deformed during D2$_M$ and a relatively undeformed resistant block of Western Lewisian gneisses in which D2$_M$ ($\equiv$ D4$_L$) structures are only weakly developed. Further west, in the mylonites of the Moine Thrust belt, tight reclined folds with an associated ESE-plunging mineral lineation are again found to be very strongly developed (Barber, 1965). Major D3$_M$ folds are present only in the eastern part of Area 2 and their western limit appears to be an extension of the "Monar front" recognised by Langford (1980) in the Beinn Dronaig area (Sheet 82). The D3$_M$ folds are thus probably equivalent to the Monar fold generation of Tobisch et al., (1970). Although major D3$_M$ structures die out towards the west post-D2$_M$ minor folds and a crenulation cleavage occur in the Eastern Lewisian (Table 4, D5$_L$), locally in slide zone 1 and in the Moine Thrust mylonites (Barber, 1965, assymetrical folding) and these structures are tentatively correlated with D3$_M$.

## AREA 3

The Strathconon Fault and a major tectonic break, correlated with the Sgurr Beag Slide, form the boundary of Area 3 which is in two parts (Figure 3). The large area around Coire nan Gall, together with a much smaller area north-east of Iron Lodge [NH 043 294], consists of Lewisian gneiss interfolded with Moine psammite and pelite.

## Stratigraphy and lithology

The Coire nan Gall area was originally mapped by Clifford (1957) who divided the Moine rocks into a Siliceous Granulitic Schist Series and a younger Garnetiferous Mica-Schist Series. He also recognised 'Lewisianoid' gneiss and a Moine Coire nan Gall Series which he regarded as forming an allochthonous sheet, emplaced during the earliest of several structural episodes, and preserved as a klippe by erosion of a later isoclinal downfold.

Remapping has shown that although a major slide bounds Area 3 there is no major tectonic break within the Coire nan Gall area and that the Moine rocks, although complexly folded, probably form a continuous stratigraphic succession. Four main divisions of metamorphic rock were distinguished and mapped (Figure 14). The succession, worked out on structural grounds, is:

Upper psammite

Pelite and striped rocks

Lower psammite

Lewisian gneiss

The Lewisian rocks are considerably more extensive in outcrop than those delineated by Clifford (1957, plate IX) and include much of the rock which he regarded as 'Coire nan Gall Series'. Direct comparison of the new units with his 'series' is, therefore, impracticable. It has not been possible to confirm any of Clifford's observations of 'way-up' based on sedimentary structures and it is probable that in this area early penetrative deformation was so intense as to have obliterated any primary structures. Consequently, the above succession cannot be proved to be a true stratigraphic one and for this reason it is considered undesirable to apply formal lithostratigraphic names. However, since it is repeated on either side of the layer of Lewisian rocks it has been concluded that the Lewisian occupies the core of a major isoclinal fold. This would suggest that the Moine youngs away the Lewisian, but it is also possible that the Lewisian now occupying the fold core was initially emplaced along a slide and is now occupying a stratigraphically anomalous position.

The lower psammite is heterogeneous, although commonly a coarse, flaggy somewhat gneissose quartzofeldspathic granulite. Locally, for example around Loch nan Eun, it contains abundant pelitic and semipelitic stripes. Elsewhere it is extremely coarse grained and micaceous, in places with a very well-defined, spaced mica lamination. A psammite, several metres thick, containing abundant quartzofeldspathic augen, of the order of a centimetre or so in length, is commonly present next to the Lewisian. This augen psammite is of interest because it is similar in many respects to the Reidh Psammite traced by Tanner (1971) in the vicinity of the Lewisian strip lying close to the Sgurr Beag Slide.

The pelite (Figure 14) is a garnetiferous mica-schist containing stripes of psammite and semipelite and muscovite porphyroblasts. Quartzofeldspathic leucosomes are present but the degree of migmatisation is generally much less than

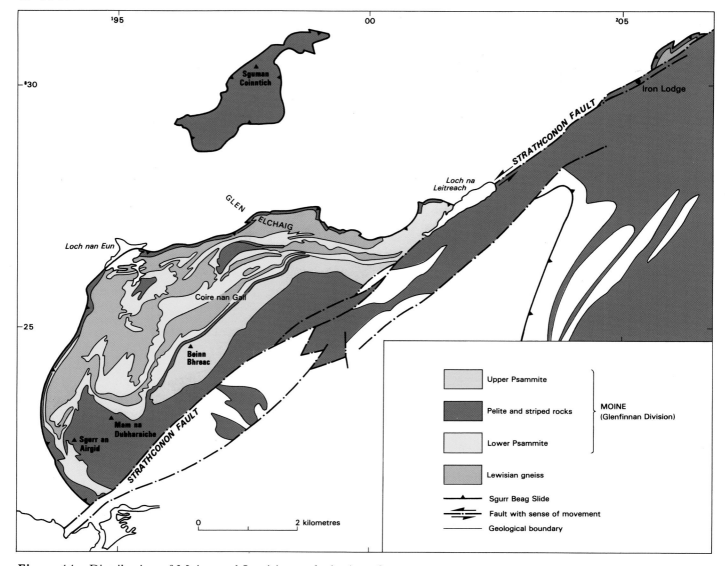

**Figure 14** Distribution of Moine and Lewisian rocks in Area 3.

in the lower psammite immediately adjacent to the Lewisian.

The upper psammite is a quartzofeldspathic granulite with micaceous partings.

The Coire nan Gall rocks are separated from adjoining areas of Moine rocks by structural breaks; a major slide on the north and west and the Strathconon Fault on the south-east. There appears to have been a sinistral horizontal movement of about 6 km on the Strathconon Fault (see p.60). However, there was also an important vertical component with downthrow to the south east which makes it impossible to exactly match outcrops on opposite sides of the fault.

From an examination of the map (Figure 14) and of the lithologies involved it is difficult to escape the conclusion that the pelite of Coire nan Gall is a displaced part of the Glenfinnan Division pelite which crops out to the south east of the fault and that it is the Sgurr Beag Slide which bounds Area 3 to the north and west. All the Moine rocks within Area 3 are, therefore, provisionally assigned to the Glenfinnan Division.

## Structure

SUMMARY OF MAIN STRUCTURAL FEATURES

The area is characterised by a complex outcrop pattern of Lewisian and Moine rocks (Figure 14) which are interpreted as an interference pattern of different sets of folds resulting from polyphase deformation. The complexity is such that it has not yet proved possible to produce an unambiguous interpretation of the whole pattern. For the purposes of description the area can be divided into two lithologically and structurally distinctive zones:

(i) A south-east zone containing only Moine rocks, both psammitic and pelitic, and is dominated by the major Beinn Bhreac synform, a tight fold with subhorizontal hinge trending north-east, overturned towards the north-west (Fleuty 1974).

(ii) A north-west zone comprising Lewisian gneiss and Moine psammite with only subordinate pelitic outcrops

(Figure 14). This zone covers approximately the same ground as the 'Kintail Klippe' of Clifford (1957) and is separated from the Moine of Area 2 by a major structural break correlated with the Sgurr Beag Slide. The major structural features are a series of variably plunging, tight folds overturned to the north-west, which fold a sequence of interbanded Lewisian and Moine strips. This zone forms the complex core of a major overturned antiform complementary to the Beinn Bhreac synform.

## D1$_M$ STRUCTURES

In the west part of Area 2 early (D1$_M$) structures are preserved and it seems probable that Area 3 was also affected by an early event, although the minor structures associated with it appear to have been completely obscured by penetrative D2$_M$ deformation. The extent and significance of this early deformation in Area 3 is thus unknown.

## D2$_M$ STRUCTURES

There is plentiful evidence that folds associated with the Beinn Bhreac synform (D3$_M$) deform earlier structures. These comprise tight to isoclinal, often intrafolial folds, with a well-developed hinge surface schistosity and an accompanying mineral lineation, striping, and rodding. They constitute the main pervasive planar and linear structures of the area. Although the hinge surface orientation of the D2$_M$ folds varies appreciably as a result of subsequent refolding, there are no comparable consistent curvatures of linear structures, which plunge to the south-east over most of the area (Figure 10). This is a result of the axial directions of the various later structures being either parallel or perpendicular to the earlier linear trends.

The rock sequence deformed by D3$_M$ folds is not a simple stratigraphic succession, since it involves interleaved Moine and Lewisian rocks. In the absence of any sedimentary structures in the Moine rocks it is not easy to decide whether this interleaving is the result of isoclinal folding, sliding, or a combination of both. Nearly all the Lewisian rocks are in outcrop continuity with each other (Figure 14) and the fact that so much of the Lewisian outcrop forms part of one body of rock is taken as evidence that it is a single folded sheet. Furthermore, there is a consistent sequence of Moine rocks reading away from the main Lewisian outcrop except for the north and north-west, where the bounding pelite is in structural contact with Lewisian rocks, whether this be structurally upwards or downwards. The sequence is: Lewisian, lower psammite, pelite, upper psammite and it is suggested that all pelite outcrops in the area belong to the same 'member' of a Moine stratigraphic succession.

It is thus concluded that the interleaving of the Moine and Lewisian is the result of isoclinal folding with very high amplitude to wavelength ratios. However, because the relationship of D2$_M$ minor structures with postulated early folds is obscure, it is not possible to decide if the folding occurred during D1$_M$ or D2$_M$ or both periods of deformation.

*The Dubharaiche folds*   The Beinn Bhreac synform, and a pair of folds further west which are also ascribed to D3$_M$, all terminate towards the south-west at a WNW–ESE belt of steeply dipping rocks forming a major south-east-plunging antiform–synform pair (the Dubharaiche folds). The relationship of these folds to other structures in the area is not clear but there is some evidence from minor structures for tentatively concluding that the Dubharaiche folds represent a phase of oblique folding which predates D3$_M$.

## D3$_M$ STRUCTURES

In the centre and north of the area, where the D3$_M$ folding is best studied, there are differences in style of the structures from south-east to north-west. Fleuty (1974) showed that the characteristic features of major and minor structures in the south-east of the area are the presence of rounded hinge zones without obvious lineation, an interlimb angle of about 30°, and SE-dipping hinge surfaces. Where micaceous rocks are involved in these folds there is commonly a hinge-surface crenulation cleavage, but no true pervasive schistosity. North-westwards, a much more pervasive hinge surface fabric is the rule, and while in the pelitic rocks it is commonly a tight crenulation, in the more psammitic rocks there is a planar orientation of micas and flattening of pre-existing quartzofeldspathic knots. This is accompanied by a linear fabric (grain-orientation and rodding) parallel to the fold hinges. Along the north margin of the western zone, and in the north-eastern part of the area the structures of this generation show evidence of even more intense deformation. For example in the crags overlooking Glen Elchaig there is a development of extremely platy zones parallel to or slightly oblique to the hinge surface fabric and replacing limbs or hinge zones of D3$_M$ folds. These phenomena are interpreted as the result of intense localised flattening contemporaneous with the D3$_M$ folding.

The plunges of the D3$_M$ folds show considerable variation over the area as a whole. In part this results from later refolding, and possible superposition across earlier folds, but variation also occurs in places where there is no clear evidence for such controls. This has been demonstrated for the Beinn Bhreac synform (Fleuty, 1974) and is apparent also in the core of the complementary antiform. In some cases it is expressed as dome and basin development, with the plunge varying through the horizontal by as much as 80°. In other cases the fold hinges show variation in attitude by increasing pitch on a reasonably constantly orientated south-east-dipping hinge surface.

The moderately dipping north-west limb of the Beinn Bhreac synform is characterised by congruous minor folds with a pattern indicating a synform to the south-east and an antiform to the north-west. This pattern persists as far as a central belt in the western zone, containing two inliers of pelite surrounded by psammite. These inliers are major domed D3$_M$ antiforms. To the north-west of this belt, dips of banding are moderate to steep and minor D3$_M$ folds have a pattern indicating structural overturning with an antiform to the south-east.

The conclusion that the western zone is a major D3$_M$ antiform has important regional implications. The mapping of rocks adjoining the Strathconon Fault indicates the pelite in Area 3 is a displaced portion of the Glenfinnan Division Pelite and that the slide bounding Area 3 is an extension of the Sgurr Beag Slide (Figure 14). In west Inverness-shire the Glenfinnan Division occupies a high structural level and was downfolded into the Morar Division during D3$_M$ deformation, for example in the Glenshian synform (Powell et al.,

1981; Baird, 1982) and in the Sguman Coinntich fold (Area 2). If the correlation across the Strathconon fault stated above is correct then the west zone of Area 3 would be expected to be synformal with a core of high-level Glenfinnan Division rocks. However, the local structural evidence indicates an antiform in this position and there is thus a major problem of interpretation which is, at present, unresolved.

## D4$_M$ STRUCTURES

Structures postdating the D3$_M$ folding occur sporadically. They are mostly east- to south-east-trending warps and kinks, with associated crenulation cleavage, and very local lineation plunging south-east, and are probably associated with the later stages of formation of the major strike arcuation of the complex.

## Metamorphic and structural history

The sequence of events affecting the Moine and Lewisian of Area 3 is outlined in Table 7. Research in the Coire nan Gall area has concentrated on structural geology and no detailed metamorphic studies have been undertaken. The fabric and mineralogy of the pelite show that the D2$_M$ deformation took place under amphibolite facies conditions. High ductility and intense flattening are indicated by the style of the D2$_M$ folds. The D3$_M$ structures suggest conditions of moderate to high ductility, perhaps during waning and locally variable metamorphic crystallisation. Essentially postmetamorphic conditions of low ductility prevailed during D4$_M$.

## AREA 4

Area 4 extends south-west and north-east of Shielbridge and is limited to the north-west by the Strathconon Fault (Figures 3 and 15). To the east, south and west the boundary of Area 4 is a slide zone separating dominantly gneissose pelitic, psammitic and mixed lithologies in which occur several thin bands and enclaves of Lewisian, from non-gneissose psammitic rocks of the Morar Division in Area 5. The gneissose rocks of Area 4 form an arcuate belt some 1–5 km wide extending from the head of Loch Duich to Glen More, at the western edge of Sheet 72W.

The Lewisian rocks of Area 4 are described in detail elsewhere (p.17) and a structural description is given below.

## Lithology

### PELITE AND SEMIPELITE

Migmatised pelitic and semipelitic rocks form large outcrops in the north-east of Area 4. They are coarsely crystalline, garnetiferous, and contain numerous quartzofeldspathic lits with subordinate bands of psammitic gneiss. The pelitic gneiss on Sgurr Mhic Bharraich [NG 915 173] contains several narrow impersistent bands of Lewisian hornblendic rock.

### MIXED ASSEMBLAGES

The pelitic and semipelitic rocks in the north-east of Area 4 pass southwards into a mixed assemblage of thinly banded (striped) pelite, semipelite and psammite. The rocks are highly gneissose as a result of the presence of numerous concordant quartzofeldspathic lits and augen and locally the quartzofeldspathic lits are so abundant that the original composition of the host rock is uncertain. Narrow bands of Lewisian, consisting of several rock types (p.17), are common in the mixed assemblages. One band of Lewisian rock has been traced almost continuously for more than 3 km along strike and is parallel to and some 100–200 m north of the slide zone defining the Area boundary.

### PSAMMITE

Non-gneissose psammite occurs in Glen More [NG 900 160] where it is truncated to the north by an offshoot of the Strathconon Fault. It is a flaggy psammite with some pelitic partings and thin bands of semipelite. Occasional calcsilicate ribs have been recorded. To the east and the south the psammite becomes very gneissose, the gneissosity being formed by the presence of numerous quartzofeldspathic lits and augen. Thin, discrete pods of Lewisian have been located in the psammite (Sheet 72W).

## Stratigraphy

The thick bands of gneissose pelite, semipelite and psammite and the large outcrops of mixed lithologies resemble the rock types of the Glenfinnan Division rather than those of the Loch Eil or Morar Division. The inclusion in these rock types of Lewisian slices shows that there are similarities to the complex Moine/Lewisian associations of Area 3 and such similarity in the Moine/Lewisian associations may imply the bounding slide of Area 4, like that of Area 3, could be a downfold of the Sgurr Beag Slide. Psammites lithologically similar to those of the Morar Division are also present, however, and it is not considered possible, on present evidence, to correlate with any certainty the Moine rocks of

**Table 7**  Sequence of events in the Moine and Lewisian of Area 3 and correlations with the Moine of Area 2.

| Area 3 | Area 2 |
|---|---|
| D4$_M$ Strike arcuation of complex and local development of minor structures | Not recognised |
| D3$_M$ Formation of major NE–SW-trending Beinn Bhreac Synform and complex complementary antiform | D3$_M$ |
| Dubharaiche folding. Formation of major, but local, antiform and synform | Not recognised |
| D1$_M$–D2$_M$ Interleaving of the Moine and Lewisian by isoclinal folding. Formation of dominant penetrative minor structure. Major sliding bringing rocks of Area 3 into contact with rocks of Area 2 | D2$_M$ D1$_M$ |
| Sedimentation of the Moine on the Lewisian basement | |

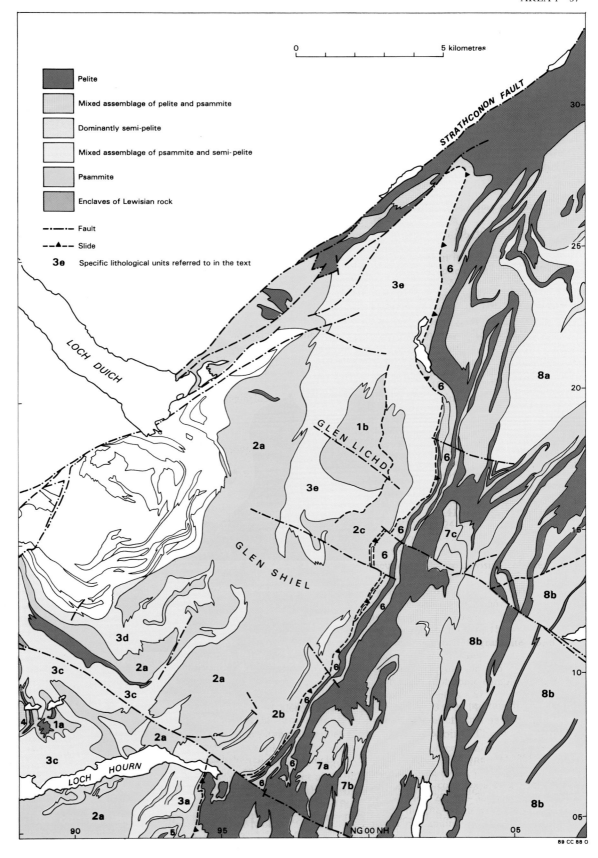

**Figure 15**
Lithological subdivisions of Areas 5 and 6, south-east of the Strathconon Fault.

Area 4; on Sheet 72W they have been doubtfully assigned to the Morar Division.

## AREA 5

The rocks of Area 5, which form a continuation of the Morar Division exposed in the type area, crop out in a belt some 7–9 km wide, limited to the east by the Sgurr Beag Slide, and to the west by the Strathconon Fault and the boundary slide of Area 4. They comprise sparsely micaceous psammites and flaggy micaceous granulites, both psammitic and semipelitic. As pointed out by Johnstone et al. (1969) the criteria used for the lithostratigraphical subdivision of this Division cannot readily be applied north-eastwards from the type area. Consequently, the lithology of the mapped units is described first and tentative stratigraphic correlations are discussed later.

### Lithology

Five main rock subdisions represented in the area are referred to by number, without implication of stratigraphical order (Figure 15). Further subdivision by letter indicates separately mapped units which are defined either on an individual outcrop basis or on some distinguishing lithological characteristic. The chief subdivisions are as follows:
1 Coarse gneissose psammite
2 Non-gneissose psammite
3 Mixed semipelite, pelite and psammite
4 As 3, but with abundant quartz veins
5 Pelite and semipelite.

#### Coarse gneissose psammite

Coarse biotite psammite, which displays a gneissosity as a result of the presence of blebs and stringers of quartz and K-feldspar material, occurs in the Dubh Lochain area (1a in Figure 15) south of the Kinlochhourn Fault. Heavy mineral concentrations occur as streaks and thick bands of coarse feldspathic pelite with bands of dark semipelite occur locally. The psammite was termed the Cosaig Psammite by Tanner (1965). Coarse, partly gneissose psammite is also developed in a dome-like structure which crosses Ben Attow and Glen Lichd (1b in Figure 15). Near its southern contact and also in much of its northern outcrop it is predominantly a coarse-grained buff to almost white-weathering rock with a few augen and concordant veinlets of quartz and feldspar, but includes also stripes of fine-grained semipelite and psammite. Towards the core of the 'dome' it becomes strongly gneissose with lit-par-lit veining by quartz and pegmatite [NH 000 180]. Calcsilicate ribs were not recorded in this psammite.

#### Non-gneissose psammite

Most of Area 5 is underlain by a continuous single outcrop of non-gneissose psammite which extends from south of Loch Hourn to north of Glen Lichd. In the south-west it is continuous with the Barrisdale Psammite of Ramsay and Spring (1962) (Table 5), which is part of the Beinn na Caillich group of Clough (in Peach et al., 1910).

Fine-grained, flaggy to massive, light grey to medium grey psammite (2a in Figure 15) forms the majority of the outcrop. More feldspathic varieties contain up to 30 per cent of K-feldspar and/or plagioclase. The variations in colour are due to greater or lesser amounts of biotite, which is the predominant mica present. Superficial reddening occurs and is the result of alteration associated with the development of closely spaced local fractures. Calcsilicate bands in the psammite are either very sparse or absent, although south of Loch Hourn unit 2a contains many ribs of quartz-zoisite or quartz-epidote rock, as well as plagioclase-rich calcsilicate lenses (Tanner, 1971).

The psammite locally contains biotite-rich semipelite, with which it may be finely interlayered, and may also include micaceous seams with small muscovite porphyroblasts. Locally the thicker semipelitic bands contain numerous ribs of calcsilicate rock as, for example, those bands in the vicinity of Lochanan Meall nan Eun [NG 905 055]. A coarse feldspathic pelite is present in the Allt Chaolas Bhig [NG 892 948] and on the south shore of Loch Hourn at the extreme west margin of Sheet 72W [NG 880 060]. At the latter locality the pelite locally contains numerous calcsilicate lenticles. Heavy mineral bands in the psammite were noted by Tanner (1971) in outcrops on both sides of Loch Hourn. North of Glen Shiel the psammite becomes generally somewhat more micaceous and calcsilicate ribs, usually sparse or absent, are more common.

North of the Kinlochhourn Fault the rocks for some 2 km west of the Sgurr Beag Slide are chiefly massive micaceous psammite with subsidiary dark semipelitic bands (2b in Figure 15) and which form part of the Coire Mhicrail Group of Tanner (1971). Both the psammites and semipelites contain calcsilicate ribs which are abundant in places. Detailed mapping on the south-east slopes of Buidhe Bheinn [NG 957 087] suggests that the relationship of the psammite to one of the larger bodies of semipelite is one of intricate isoclinal folding, one rock passing into the other along the strike and, locally, the junction of units 2a and 2b is a tectonic break which truncates the lithological banding in 2b (Peacock and Berridge, 1971). In Glen Shiel unit 2b is well exposed in road cuttings.

On the north slopes of Glen Shiel the firm distinction between units 2a and 2b is lost and the strata pass laterally into unit 2c which is composed of (a) massive grey sparsely micaceous psammite without calcsilicate ribs, (b) grey, micaceous and sparsely micaceous psammite with numerous calcsilicate ribs and a few bands of semipelite and (c) psammite interbanded and laminated with subsidiary semipelite with calcsilicate ribs sparingly distributed. Lithology (a) is well seen on the south side of the valley of the Allt a'Choire Dhomhain [NG 998 158] (b) in the Allt an Lapain [NH 010 157] and (c) in the Allt Granda [NH 0167 170] and in a belt surrounding unit 1b in the Glen Lichd area.

Cross-bedding and other sedimentary structures have been recorded at several localities within the outcrop of the non-gneissose psammite and provide some evidence that, in general, the succession youngs eastwards (cf. Tanner, 1971, p.441). Penecontemporaneous slump folds and conglomerates are visible in psammites exposed in the River Shiel upstream of the road bridge [NH 113 132].

#### Mixed semipelite, pelite and psammite

Strata composed of mixed interbanded psammite, semipelite and pelite are distributed as thick units within the non-gneissose psammites of subdivision 2. They form large outcrops north and south of Loch Hourn, and in the area north of Glen Shiel and Ben Attow (published Sheet 72W).

South of Loch Hourn unit 3a is composed of psammite interbedded with significant, and in places dominant, dark thinly flaggy micaceous rocks with laminae and bands varying from a few millimetres to a few metres thick of highly biotitic psammite, feldspathic psammite, semipelite and pelite (3a in Figure 15). These rocks, which form part of the Coire Mhicrail Group of Tanner (1971), carry abundant ribs of calcsilicate (up to 3 ribs per metre) and can be correlated in general terms with the more psammitic strata of unit 2 on the north side of Loch Hourn.

West of unit 3a there is a further broad outcrop of striped, banded and laminated psammite, semipelite and pelite, locally with abundant calcsilicate ribs (3c in Figure 15). These beds, the Druim Fada Group of Tanner (1965), underlie the sparsely micaceous Barrisdale Psammite proper (2a) and have a complex outcrop pattern in the Dubh Lochain area. The apparently simple younging pattern is reversed in zones, commonly fairly wide, as a result of tight and isoclinal folding on all scales. A pod of hornblende-bearing gneiss of Lewisian type occurs in this group north of the Kinlochhourn Fault [NG 925 100].

In the Saddle area [NG 936 128] the broad outcrop of mixed psammite and semipelite (3d) is lithologically similar to unit 3c, but calcsilicate ribs are sparse. The rock is locally accompanied by numerous concordant quartzofeldspathic leucosomes, but in contrast to the psammites of subdivision 1 there is no coarsening of grain size.

Thinly flaggy semipelite and psammite (3e in Figure 15), which lithologically resembles the more micaceous parts of unit 3a at Kinlochhourn, forms a broad outcrop north of Ben Attow [NH 019 193]. It contains numerous calcsilicate ribs in places and there are small muscovite porphyroblasts in the micaceous seams. Cross-bedding showing that the strata locally face east occurs at two nearby localities [NH 013 237]. Similar rocks, but with fewer calcsilicate ribs, occur in a belt extending along the Five Sisters of Kintail ridge, northwards from Sgurr na Carnach [NG 976 159] and Sgurr na Ciste Dubh [NG 983 140]. This outcrop includes massive micaceous psammite and bands of striped garnetiferous pelite. Heavy mineral laminae occur in the psammite at a locality [NG 993 224] near Dorusduain.

MIXED SEMIPELITE, PELITE AND PSAMMITE WITH ABUNDANT QUARTZ VEINS

This assemblage of pelite, semipelite and micaceous psammite, which is characterised by abundant contorted quartz veins, is confined to the Dubh Lochain area [NG 886 095]. The significance of this outcrop is discussed below.

PELITE AND SEMIPELITE

In the core of the Sgurr nan Eugallt Fold south-east of Sgurr Sgiath Airidh [NG 926 053] there is a coarse semipelitic and pelitic gneiss with calcsilicate ribs. This subdivision, which is separated from unit 3a by a band of calcsilicate-bearing psammite, can be directly correlated with the lower two units of the Morar Schists (Table 5), which overlie the Lower Morar Psammite of the type area (Johnstone et al., 1969).

## Stratigraphy

The survey has shown that one important criterion used to establish the stratigraphic successions south of Loch Hourn, the presence or absence of calcsilicates, is, because of their widespread and sporadic distribution, of little stratigraphic application north of Loch Hourn and firm correlations with the successions established in Knoydart and Morar cannot be proposed with any degree of confidence. In general, it is probably best to consider the whole of Area 5, with the possible exception of some of subdivison 3 (see below) as belonging to the Lower Morar Psammite (Table 5). Units 1a and possibly 1b may be equivalent, in general terms, to the Arnisdale Psammitic Group of Loch Hourn (Ramsay and Spring, 1962, and Table 5). The coarse, somewhat gneissose psammite 1a (Figure 15), equivalent to the Cosaig Psammite of Tanner (1965), contains thick bands of pelite. It most closely resembles the coarse siliceous psammitic gniesses which, with subordinate pelite, occur in North Morar to the south-east of Kyles Knoydart, and which have been regarded as equivalent to the Arnisdale Psammitic Group (Sheet 61). In the present area it is in contact with unit 3c which locally contains numerous calcsilicates.

The rocks around the Dubh Lochain [e.g. NG 890 095] and designated 4 on Figure 14 have a lithology similar in many aspects to that of the Basal Semi-Pelite (Ramsay and Spring, 1962), or the Main and Subsidiary Striped Group (Richey and Kennedy, 1939) of Knoydart and Morar. The mapping of Ramsay and Spring (1962) and Tanner (1965), however, suggests these rocks should be correlated with the semipelites within the Arnisdale and Barrisdale psammites (Lower Morar Psammite of Johnstone et al., 1969) of Knoydart/Glenelg. If unit 4 is not the Basal Semi-Pelite of the Moine, then it is possible that the only representative of the Basal Semi-Pelite in the area of the Dubh Lochain is the unit bordering the eastern side of the Lewisian outcrop between the Dubh Lochain and Bealach Aoidhdailean [NG 884 121]. This rock is only a few metres thick and consists largely of grey granulite and schists. It is commonly rich in biotite and may be a Lewisian – Moine tectonic hybrid.

Turning to the area adjacent to the Sgurr Beag Slide it is probable that the psammite (2 in Figure 15) belongs to the Lower Morar Psammite but the affinities of the adjacent unit 3a are less clear. Tanner (1971, pl. 29) links unit 3a and the psammite between 3a and 5 with the Ladhar Beinn Pelite (equivalent to only part of the Morar Schists — see Johnstone et al. (1969 and Table 5), and suggests it is an eastern facies equivalent of the lower part of this pelitic group. On Sheet 62 (Lochaber) however, the Morar Schists in the core of the Sgurr nan Eugallt Fold (5 in Figure 15) belong to the lowest two members of this tripartite sequence. Unit 3a of Figure 15, together with the psammite between 3a and 5, which jointly form the 'Coire Mhicrail Group' of Tanner, 1971, would thus be the upper part of the Lower Morar Psammite. The position is further complicated by the possible intervention of a slide, the Knoydart Slide, which attenuates the succession of the Morar Schists and the Lower Morar Psammite west of the present area (Johnstone et al., 1969, Powell, 1974). North-east of Buidhe Bheinn [NG 957 087] attenuation of a semipelite at the western limit of abundant calcsilicates suggests the possibility that the Knoydart

Slide extends north of Loch Hourn. Structural complexities are also indicated by the pod of Lewisian material in unit 3c north of the Kinlochhourn Fault. The folded contact of a body of semipelite south-east of Buidhe Bheinn with the neighbouring psammite has already been noted.

As with the lower part of the Lower Morar Psammite, discussed above (unit 1a), lithological evidence, in particular that offered by the distribution of calcsilicates, suggests that some of the criteria used to establish the Moine stratigraphy in Knoydart (Ramsay and Spring, 1962) cannot be readily applied to the Kintail area. In the Knoydart/Glenelg region (Ramsay and Spring, 1962), calcsilicate ribs were not recorded below a horizon low in the Ladhar Beinn Pelite, that is, within the upper two members of the tripartite Morar Schists of the standard Morar succession (Richey and Kennedy, 1939, Johnstone et al., 1969 and Table 5). In north-east Morar, however, calcsilicates extend to the base of the Morar Schists, suggesting that the lower limit of calcsilicates has extended downwards in an easterly direction. This downward migration has clearly continued northwards to Kinlochhourn, and in Glen Shiel has evidently extended well down into the sparsely micaceous psammite characteristic of much of the Lower Morar Psammite. It seems likely therefore, that the presence of calcsilicates, although a valuable local stratigraphical criterion, has to be treated with considerable reserve when put to widespread application.

## AREA 6

The rocks of area 6 are northward continuations of the Glenfinnan Division rocks exposed in the type area on Sheet 62. They are limited to the west by the Sgurr Beag Slide and extend to the eastern limit of the Sheet where they are continuous with rocks of the Glenfinnan Division in Sheet 72E. The Division comprises thick units of psammite, generally more common in the east, thick bands of pelite and wide mappable units of mixed lithologies, made up of intimately interbanded horizons of pelite, semipelite and psammite. Only a very few sedimentary structures have been identified, within the thick psammites of the east, and a stratigraphic succession within Area 6 has not been established. While individual units can be traced for several kilometres along strike the outcrop pattern is complex, due to lateral passage between rock types along strike and to the effects of polyphase folding.

## Lithology

### Pelite and mixed lithologies

The Glenfinnan Division is characterised in part by thick bands of coarse pelite which in many areas contain migmatitic lits and augen of quartz and plagioclase. These locally impart a gneissosity to the rock, as, for example, south of Kinlochhourn [NG 95 07] and in the valley of the Allt Granda [NG 927 170]. Muscovite porphyroblasts are common at some localities [NH 020 130]. The area of pelite immediately south of the Strathconon Fault in the north-east of the area can be followed across the adjoining Sheet 72E to the north flank of An Riabhachan (Sheet 82), where it is in

contact with a large body of Lewisian rocks. The pelite contains local enclaves of gneissose psammite and striped and banded lithologies. Calcsilicate bands are uncommon. From the wide outcrop of pelite in the north-east pelitic bands can be followed southwards, parallel to the trace of the Sgurr Beag Slide, as far as Kinlochhourn, where the name Sgurr Beag Pelite was applied by Tanner (1971). Pelite and associated mixed lithologies also occur in the outcrop of the Easter Glen Quoich Psammite (see below), in the south-east part of the mapped area.

The mixed assemblages of pelite, semipelite and psammite include not only lithologies interbanded on a scale too small to be mapped out, but distinctive striped and banded rocks consisting of sharply defined bands of pelite and psammite, up to 10 cm thick and characteristic of the Glenfinnan Striped Schists of the type area (Johnstone et al., 1969). Calcsilicate lenticles are common in this rock type, but less so than in parts of the Morar Division referred to above. Examples of this 'Glenfinnan Striped' type of lithology are well seen near the track 1 km north-west of Alltbeithe [NH 021 072] and in Glen Shiel near the mouth of the Allt a' Choire Reidh [NH 024 125]. Another variety of striped and banded schists, well seen in the Wester Glen Quoich Burn west of Alltbeithe, consists of laminated micaceous and siliceous psammite with pelitic partings 1 to 10 cm in thickness and sparse calcsilicate ribs. Other laminated rocks composed of micaceous psammite, semipelite and pelite, lack calcsilicates but commonly develop large muscovite porphyroblasts in the micaceous seams.

### Psammite, including some semipelitic rocks

The psammites immediately east of the Sgurr Beag Slide (6 in Figure 15) are distinguished from those of the Morar Division by their yellow-brown weathering and by the relative coarseness of grain size. The psammites are generally gneissose, due to the presence of quartzofeldspathic (mainly microcline) augen and thin concordant lits which vary greatly in level of abundance. Calcsilicates, although present, are rare. Simony (1963) and Tanner (1971) reported laminae of heavy minerals, including magnetite, in the psammite (the Reidh Psammite) between Kinlochhourn and Glen Shiel. The more feldspathic psammites include both plagioclase-rich and K-feldspar-rich varieties. Laminated platy micaceous K-feldspar-rich psammite with green hornblende, epidote-allanite and sphene has been noted at one locality, about 200 m east of the Sgurr Beag Slide [NG 981 095]. Although this may be an integral part of the Moine, the possibility cannot be overlooked that it may be a tectonically introduced slice of Lewisian, similar in origin to other Lewisian slices located to the north.

Several large bodies of psammite crop out in the mixed lithology assemblages. The psammite between Sgurr Mhaoraich [NG 983 076] and Coire Glas [NG 990 085] (7a in Figure 15) is chiefly a coarse-grained, feldspathic, non-gneissose psammite with a few thin bands of semipelite. Parts are muscovitic and it includes rocks in which K-feldspar and plagioclase occur in roughly equal amounts. The band of psammite to the east (7b in Figure 15) is also non-gneissose, being chiefly laminated micaceous psammite with muscovite porphyroblasts in the micaceous seams. Locally bands of quartzite occur. On the north side of Glen

Shiel, however, the folded muscovite- and biotite-bearing psammite at the head of Sreath an Fhraoch-choire (7c in Figure 15) is markedly gneissose with concordant quartzo-feldspathic lits throughout the outcrop.

The major psammite body in the Glenfinnan Division is the Easter Glen Quoich Psammite (Geological Survey of Great Britain, Summary of Progress for 1964, p.69). In the northern parts of the outcrop (8a in Figure 15) it is generally a dark, micaceous to highly micaceous psammite with locally many bands of pelite and semipelite and calcsilicate lenticles in places. Bands within the psammite contain muscovite porphyroblasts. 'Wispy' folds of possible sedimentary origin have been seen, but undoubted sedimentary structures have not been recorded in these northern outcrops. Southwards unit 8a passes into the major outcrop of the Easter Glen Quoich Psammite (unit 8b) across the summit of Ciste Dhubh [NH 063 166]. In the east, in the type area in Easter Glen Quoich, unit 8b can be subdivided as in Table 8 and

**Table 8**  Lithology of unit 8b (Easter Glen Quoich Psammite) in Easter Glen Quoich.

| | Thickness (m) |
|---|---|
| (Structural top of succession to west) | |
| 11 Laminated micaceous and sparsely micaceous psammite with quartzite bands up to 7 m thick. Rare thin bands of pelite | 213 |
| 10 Semipelite and pelite with bands of quartzite and psammite | 67 |
| 9 Laminated micaceous and sparsely micaceous psammite with thin (1 m) bands of quartzite | 460 |
| 8 (c) Striped garnetiferous pelite | 60 |
| (b) Banded micaceous and sparsely micaceous psammite with subsidiary bands of semipelite | 90 |
| (a) Striped garnetiferous pelite | 45 |
| 7 Laminated micaceous and sparsely micaceous psammite with ribs and bands of quartzite up to 2.5 m thick. A few ribs of pelite and semipelite. Local calcsilicate nodules. Muscovite porphyroblasts in semipelite bands towards base | 490 |
| 6 Quartzite with subsidiary bands of sparsely micaceous and micaceous psammite and semipelite | 107 |
| 5 Laminated micaceous and sparsely micaceous psammite with subordinate ribs and bands of semipelite locally up to 20 m thick. Calcsilicate lens towards base | 790 |
| 4 Coarse, dominantly sparsely micaceous psammite with concordant lenticles of pink pegmatite up to 5 cm thick. ?Calcsilicate nodules | 340 |
| 3 Semipelite and gneissose pelite with subsidiary bands of laminated micaceous and sparsely micaceous psammite | 120 |
| 2 Sparsely micaceous and micaceous psammite with numerous bands of pelite and semipelite up to 2 m thick. Quartz-feldspar augen and muscovite porphyroblasts developed in some bands | 340 |
| 1 Sparsely micaceous psammite and quartzite with semipelite bands. Magnetite streaks occur about 150 m from the top of the unit | 1710 |
| (Structural base of succession to east) | |

Figure 15. Sedimentary structures, including cross-bedding and anastomosing micaceous laminae (possibly flaser bedding) have been seen at several localities on Sheet 72W, but they are insufficient to confirm that all the units are in their original stratigraphic order.

The Easter Glen Quoich Psammite is folded by a major southward-closing fold which, when traced to the south, becomes the $D3_M$ synform that controls the outcrop pattern of the Glen Dessary Syenite (Roberts et al., 1984). The west limb of the fold is notably attenuated compared to the east limb and also contains pelite bands not found on the east limb. Hence the succession within the psammite is either structural or there are rapid facies variations along the strike.

## Stratigraphy

Because of the absence of marker horizons the very sparse sedimentary structures and the structural complexity it has not been possible to place the various lithologies within the Glenfinnan Division in stratigraphical order. To the south, on Sheet 62, Johnstone et al. (1969, p.165) originally subdivided the Glenfinnan Division into two main groups — the Lochailort Pelite overlain by the Glenfinnan Striped Schists. The former is in mapped continuity with the thicker bands of coarse pelite in the present area and the latter is lithologically identical to some of the striped rocks described above. No evidence has been found which bears on the suggestion by Brown et al. (1970, table 2) that the Glenfinnan Division rocks can be divided into four formations which become younger from west to east.

## STRUCTURE OF AREAS 4, 5 AND 6

### Introduction

The rocks of both the Morar and Glenfinnan divisions have undergone complex polyphase deformation and major and minor folds of each deformation phase have been recognised. At least three main fold episodes have been identified. The two divisions are separated by a tectonic break, the Sgurr Beag Slide, which was first described from the southern part of Sheet 72W (Tanner, 1971). Rocks of both divisions are generally steeply dipping and are locally vertical. In the Glenfinnan Division an obvious structural feature is the presence of tight, long-limbed folds with axial traces that can be identified over distances of several kilometres (Figure 16). In the Morar Division large open-style folds with variable axial plunge refold earlier folds on both the large and small scale and give rise to broad changes in the orientation of the foliation.

For descriptive purposes two main episodes of folding are considered; 'early folds', of $D2_M$ age or earlier, and 'late folds' of $D3_M$ age or later. Each episode has major folds and related minor folds. The following account describes the structural features within the rocks of the Morar Division of Areas 4 and 5, followed by a description of the structures within the Glenfinnan Division of Area 6.

**Figure 16**
Axial traces of major folds in Areas 4, 5 and 6.

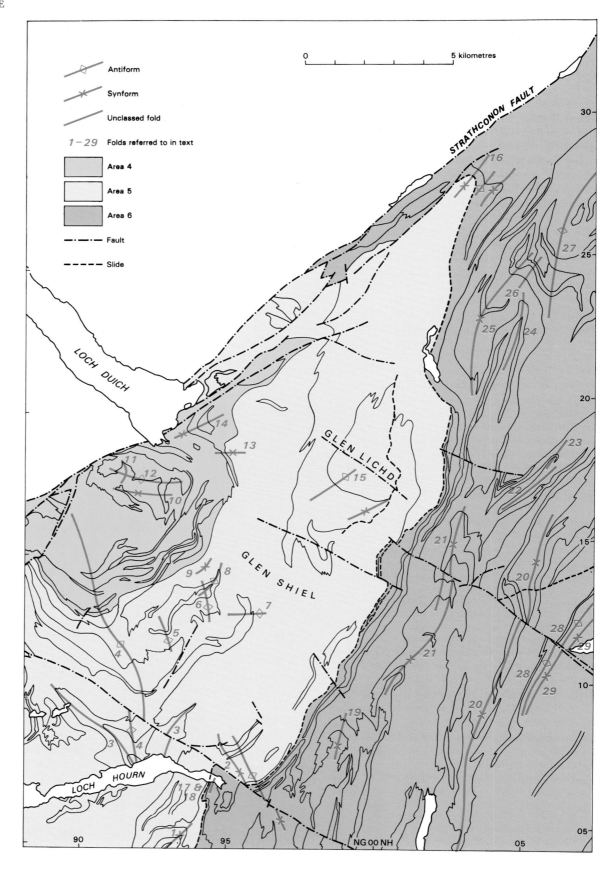

## Folds in Areas 4 and 5

EARLY FOLDS

South of Loch Hourn the rocks west of the Sgurr Beag Slide are folded by fold 1 (Figure 16) which is the northward continuation of the major D2 Sgurr nan Eugalt–Slat Bheinn fold, well seen in the ground immediately south of Sheet 72W. It is a synformal, northward-closing structure, with an axial plane dipping steeply south-east (Tanner, 1971).

The minor folds associated with fold 1 refold earlier minor folds and the major closure is, therefore, attributed to the second deformation $D2_M$ (Summary of Progress for 1961; Tanner, 1965, 1971). Pelitic bands in the core of fold 1 exhibit axial-plane schistosity. Tanner (1971) reported that the Sgurr Beag Slide was folded by fold 1.

Most of the ground on the north side of Loch Hourn and to the west of Torr a'Choit [NG 932 078] lies on the south-west limb of the late fold 4 (Figure 16; Table 9). Both the outcrop pattern and detailed structural investigations here suggest that rocks which lie in this limb were involved in two episodes of folding before the imposition of the major late fold structure. Tight isoclinal infolds ($D1_M$) of pelite within unit 1a of Figure 15 (the Cosaig Psammite) in the Dubh Lochain area are folded by tight folds ($D2_M$) which in this area trend WNW. Eastwards across the axial trace of fold 4 the $D2_M$ folds, including the closure zone of fold 3, turn to run north-east, parallel to the trace of fold 1 (Tanner, 1971). In National Grid squares [NG 89 08] and [NG 90 08] non-cylindrical minor folds with a variable plunge along fold axes are refolded by late folds of the same generation as fold 4.

On the south-west limb of fold 4, in the area west of Sgurr Mhic Bharraich [NG 917 174], the gently dipping Moine gneisses with Lewisian sheets and pods are strongly affected by south-east plunging sideways closing folds with axial-plane schistosity parallel to the regional foliation. They are accompanied by strong rodding of the quartzofeldspathic lits. These $D2_M$ folds, which are more or less coaxial with the late $D4_M$ minor folds, fold the gneissosity in the pelitic rocks. Further south-east folds 8 and 9, respectively a synform and antiform, are early $D2_M$ folds identified on the north-east limb of the late fold 4 (Figure 16). They are tight to isoclinal folds with associated quartz rodding and minor folds. Both have been refolded by late folds (see below) with coaxial rodding in quartz and quartzofeldspathic veinlets. Fold 11, south-west of Shiel Bridge, is an early $D2_M$ fold, of the same generation as folds 8 and 9, which has been refolded by east–west-trending late folds (Figure 16).

North of Glen Shiel no major early folds have been traced with certainty, although their presence may account for the disposition of lithologies in some cases, for instance the tongue of pelite which extends from locality [NG 953 185] to [NG 957 173], on the east side of Glen Shiel. Minor tight to isoclinal folds, probably of the $D2_M$ generation are, however, common between Glen Shiel and Glen Lichd. They are accompanied by an axial-plane schistosity in pelites but in psammites a bedding-plane schistosity can be traced around the fold closures in micaceous laminae; the micas are also oriented parallel to the axial planes of the folds. Identical tight to isoclinal minor folds with axial-plane schistosity also occur within the lithological banding on the north side of lithological subdivision 1b on Ben Attow [NH 018 193].

LATE FOLDS

The structure of the south-west part of the area is dominated by the late stage fold 4 ($D4_M$), here termed the Bealach a'Chasain Fold. The axial trace of this fold can be traced from the Strathconon Fault SSE to near Loch Hourn where it is displaced dextrally by the Kinlochourn Fault (Figure 16).

North of the Kinlochhourn Fault the western limb of this structure dips at an average of 60° to the north-east and the other limb dips at an average of 35° towards the south-east. The axial surface is accompanied by a strong schistosity in the closure zone of the structure (Table 9). On the south-west slopes of The Saddle [NG 935 131] the fold is accompanied by a strong rodding and by contortion of the concordant quartzofeldspathic veins. Folds 2, 5 and 6 (Figure 16) are subsidiary structures associated with the Bealach a'Chasain Fold. Fold 2 and a complementary antiform to the north-east fold the Sgurr Beag Slide. Folds 5 and 6 refold the axial zones of the early folds 8 and 9.

Further north, folds 7, 10, 12, 13 and 14 are generally west- to east-trending open structures which are coaxial with folds 4, 5 and 6, and with early minor folds. Simony (1973) regarded folds 4 and 12 as coeval, forming an antiformal conjugate fold which refold early major folds, a structural interpretation that is supported by the present survey.

In the Glen Lichd area the structures in the area of lithological subdivision 1b (Figure 15) have not been fully elucidated. Fold 15 is an open antiform probably of the same generation as the late ($D4_M$) folds discussed above. The tight synform immediately to the south could, however, be either an early $D2_M$ fold or a late possibly $D4_M$ structure. The distribution of lithologies in this neighbourhood suggests the presence of major north–south-trending early or late folds, which have been disrupted by a north–south-trending slide zone, discussed below.

## Folds in Area 6

Rocks of the Glenfinnan Division in Area 6 have been subjected to more than two major periods of folding, of which the later generations ($D2_M$ and $D3_M$) are locally similar in style and orientation. It has not been possible to map out major early closures ($D1_M$) except in a few areas locally, although the presence of such early folds may be indicated indirectly by the lack of symmetry across the axial zones of the later major folds. Lack of symmetry, however, may also be the result of tectonic sliding, or by lateral facies changes.

EARLY FOLDS

Folds 22 and 23 are major early folds ($D2_M$) which can be traced for several kilometres (Figure 16 and Table 10). These folds, together with another possible early closure immediately to the west, appear to be refolded by the major $D3_M$ Sgurr an Lochain fold 21 (see below). Farther east a major early closure seen in the Glen Affric area (Sheet 72E), at locality [NH 096 166], may extend south-westwards into the map area parallel to and a short distance west of fold 28. This closure is accompanied by tight to isoclinal minor folds with attenuated limbs; they fold the bedding/foliation in psammite and are accompanied by a strong axial plane-foliation in pelitic units.

**Table 9** Summary of data on major folds in Areas 4 and 5

| Fold | | Style | Axial plane | | Plunge | Other features |
|---|---|---|---|---|---|---|
| | | | Strike | Dip | | |
| 2 | Synform | Tight to open | NW | Almost vertical | Steeply SE | Local crenulation cleavage, tight to open minor folds with associated mineral lineation |
| 4 | Antiform almost reclined | Open | North | 40° east | 35° SE | Crenulation cleavage or axial-plane schistosity. Rodding in quartz-feldspar veins parallel to plunge |
| 5 | Antiform | Tight to open | North and NNW | Steeply east | 50°–60° SSE | Local axial-plane schistosity. Rodding in quartz-feldspar veins parallel to plunge. Refold earlier minor isoclinal folds |
| 6 | Synform | | | | | |
| 7 | Antiform sideways closing | Open | ESE | 50° south | 50° SSE | Minor folds and rodding coaxial with fold 6 |
| 8 | Downward closing | Tight to isoclinal | — | — | Variable | Accompanying minor folds and rodding plunge south |
| 12 | Antiform | Open | ESE | Steeply south | 30° ESE | Local rodding in quartz-feldspar lits parallel to plunge. Refolds major tight fold (11). Local crenulation cleavage |
| 14 | Synform | Open | East | Steeply south | 30° ESE | Tight zig-zag minor folds, mineral lineation, rodding in quartz veins |
| 15 | Antiform | Open | N60°E | Steeply SE | Steeply SE | Minor folds plunge between east and south |
| 16 | Synform | Tight to open | NE | Steeply SE | 35°–50° SSW | Crenulation cleavage in pelite. Rodding in quartz-feldspar veins parallel to plunge. Folds intrafolial folds |

In the extreme south-east of the map area within the Easter Glen Quoich Psammite (8b on Figure 15), detailed structural work at several localities has shown that zones occur, up to 300 m wide, in which D2$_M$ deformation is weak. One such zone at locality [NH 056 057], trending north-east, is characterised by the occurrence of long-limbed isoclinal folds (D1$_M$). Near the margins of such zones, D2$_M$ folding becomes more obvious and the rocks are transected by well-developed foliation surfaces (S2) which occur as narrow zones or single planes spaced from 5 to 20 m apart. These constitute the most conspicuous plane of parting in the rocks.

In the area between Kinloch Hourn and Wester Glen Quoich, immediately east of the Sgurr Beag Slide, Tanner (1972) recorded major D1$_M$ folds in unit 6 and the interbanded pelite (Figure 15). No evidence bearing on the relative age of these closures was found during the geological survey, but in view of the intense D2$_M$ and D3$_M$ folding in the area generally the possibility must be considered that Tanner's D1$_M$ folds could be either D2$_M$ or D3$_M$ in the terminology used in this account.

LATE FOLDS

Near Kinloch Hourn the Moine and Lewisian rocks a short distance east of the Sgurr Beag Slide are folded by late folds (D3$_M$) comprising a synform to the west (fold 17) and an antiform to the east (fold 18; Table 10). Two tight to isoclinal folds on the west limb of fold 17 have been variously classified as D1$_M$ (Tanner, 1971) or D2$_M$ (Tanner, in discussion, Proceeding of the Geological Society, No. 1664 p.261) and D3$_M$ in the present account.

Folds 19, 20 and 21 (Figure 16 and Table 10) are major D3$_M$ folds. Fold 20 is the northward continuation of the D3$_M$ Glen Dessary–Gleouraich Synform (Roberts and Harris, 1983, Roberts et al., 1984) which has been interpreted as a sheath fold. The varying plunge along the strike of associated non-refolded minor folds within the present area supports this interpretation. In the Kintail district there is a lack of symmetry across the fold closure, with a marked reduction in thickness of the Easter Glen Quoich Psammite (8b) on the west limb.

The D3$_M$ Sgurr an Lochain (fold 21 on Figure 16), is a northwards-closing long-limbed very tight fold with a

**Table 10**
Summary of data on major folds in Area 6

| Fold | | Style | Axial plane | | Plunge | Other features |
|---|---|---|---|---|---|---|
| | | | Strike | Dip | | |
| 17 | Synform reclined | Open | NNE | Steeply ESE | Steeply east or ESE | Axial-plane crenulation cleavage in pelite. Rodding. Refold earlier folds |
| 18 | Antiform reclined | | | | | |
| 19 | Synform | Tight | NNE | Steeply ESE | Moderately south | Crenulations and local axial-plane schistosity in pelite. Plunge of minor folds varies considerably in a short distance |
| 20 | Synformal in part, sideways (southward) closing | Tight to isoclinal | NNE | Steeply ESE | Steeply to gently NNE | Axial-plane schistosity or crenulation cleavage in pelite. Plunge of minor folds varies considerably in a short distance. Minor folds refold early minor isoclines |
| 21 | Synformal to sideways (northwards) closing | Tight to isoclinal | NNE | Steeply ESE | Steeply to gently between east south | Axial-plane schistosity or crenulation cleavage in pelite. Quartzofeldspathic augen flattened in schistosity, which may be overgrown by muscovite porphyroblasts. Tight minor folds refold early isoclinal folds |
| 22 | Sideways | Isoclinal | NE | Steeply SE | Variable | Axial-plane schistosity in pelite. Minor structures reclined to inclined, horizontal |
| 23 | closing | | | | | |
| 25 | Synform to sideways (southward) closing | Tight to isoclinal | North to NNE | Steeply ESE or east | Steeply ESE to SSE | Associated rodding in quartz veins |
| 27 | Antiform to sideways closing | Open to tight | NE | Steeply SE | Moderate to SSW | Local crenulation cleavage. Tight to open minor folds with associated rodding. Minor folds refold earlier isoclinal folds with axial-plane schistosity |

rounded hinge zone (Table 10). It can be traced NNE from east of Sgurr an Lochain [NH 007 104] through Glen Shiel, into Upper Glen Lichd. The associated minor folds are well exposed in the road cutting near the junction of the Allt a Choire Reidh with the River Shiel [NH 025 125], and the closure zone is seen on slab outcrops some 300 m to the SSW. In the road cutting a strong schistosity (S3), dipping steeply ESE, is commonly developed oblique to the bedding and is axial planar to reclined minor folds in a striped pelite and psammite unit with calcsilicate ribs. The style of the minor folds varies from tight to open. Locally, there is a lineation oblique to the fold axes, and the axial plane schistosity is in places overgrown by muscovite porphyroblasts. On the slab outcrops referred to above there are numerous examples of minor folds associated with the Sgurr an Lochain fold (fold 21), refolding tight or isoclinal minor folds ($D2_M$). Downstream of these outcrops an S3 schistosity is crossed by a coarse pucker cleavage striking 110° and dipping 50°S. The folds accompanying the pucker cleavage are open folds ($D4_M$) of the same style as the late east-trending folds in lower Glen Shiel.

Further north folds 25, 26 and 27 are typical late $D3_M$ closures (Figure 16 and Table 10) which refold early major closures. Fold 24 is probably the southward continuation of fold 26.

CORRELATION OF FOLDS IN AREAS 4, 5 AND 6

Referring to Table 11, the folds of the generation represented by the Bealach a'Chasain Fold (fold 4) in Area 5, continue across the Sgurr Beag Slide into Area 6, where they refold the $D2_M/D3_M$ structural succession. This is taken as firm evidence that the late folds in Areas 4 and 5 postdate the late D3 structures identified in Area 6. Folds that could be correlated with the D3 structures of Area 6 have not been positively identified in Areas 4 and 5, although fold 16 (Figure 16) has a similar trend and style.

In Areas 4, 5 and 6 the $D2_M$ folds are correlated on the basis of similarity of style, their associated cleavages or schistosity, and their relationship to $D1_M$. The Sgurr Beag Slide is reported to be folded by $D2_M$ (Tanner et al., 1970), and folds predating, or contemporaneous with, early movement on the slide may have been initiated in areas many tens of kilometres apart and thus may not be necessarily coeval.

**Tectonic slides**

The fold episodes described above cannot satisfactorily account for the complex disposition of some rock types, including inliers of Lewisian rock, and the structural history of Areas 4, 5 and 6, and indeed of the whole of Sheet 72W, includes a period of development of tectonic slides (ductile

**Table 11** Tentative correlation of folds in Areas 4, 5 and 6

|        | Areas 4 and 5 | Area 6 |
|--------|---------------|--------|
| D4$_M$ | Folds 2, 4, 5, 6, 7, 10 12, 13 and 14 | 1  Late open folds with W–E-trending axial planes and crenulation cleavage in Glen Shiel<br>2  Open folds of fold 4 generation fold F2/F3 structures east and SE of Kinloch Hourn |
| D3$_M$ | Fold 16 | Folds 17, 18, 19, 20, 21, 22, 25, 26 and 27 |
| D2$_M$ | Folds 1, 3, 8, 9 and 11 | Folds 22 and 23. Ubiquitous minor folds |
| D1$_M$ | Local minor folds; bedding-plane schistosity | Local minor folds accompanied by schistosity |

thrusts). Such slides disrupt the stratigraphy and are responsible for the emplacement of some, if not most, of the inliers of Lewisian rocks into their present position at various levels within the Moine succession. Movement along the slides was probably synmetamorphic, and the rocks have undergone complete recrystallisation since the slide movement ceased. Obvious cataclastic or mylonitic effects resulting from slide movement are absent, although in Area 2, north of the Strathconon Fault a 'slide rock' has developed within the slide plane zones (p.28), and Rathbone and Harris (1979) describe obvious increase in the platiness of rocks adjacent to slide zones.

During the survey of Sheet 72W evidence for the presence of tectonic slides has emerged from several areas and major slide zones have been recognised as forming the boundary between Areas 2 and 3, 4 and 5 and between 5 and 6. Other slides have been recognised within the Moine succession of the Morar Division, the eastern limit of which is defined by the Sgurr Beag Slide, regarded as a tectonic break of regional significance and extent.

SGURR BEAG SLIDE

Evidence for the existence of this tectonic break was first described during the geological survey of the Barrisdale area in Sheet 62W (Geological Survey of Great Britain, Summaries of Progress for 1962–1964). Further independent evidence for its existence was given by Tanner (1965) from Kinloch Hourn and by Simony (1963) from Glen Shiel. The geographical extent and probable regional significance of the Sgurr Beag Slide has been discussed by Johnstone et al. (1969), Tanner et al. (1970), Powell (1974), Rathbone and Harris (1979) and Powell et al. (1981).

In the Barrisdale area of Sheet 62W the presence of the slide was first deduced from the obvious asymmetry between the stratigraphic succession on the north-west limb of the Sgurr nan Eugalt-Slat Bheinn fold (fold 1) and the attenuated complex succession of the south-east limb. Tanner

(1971) described obvious lithological differences between the known stratigraphic succession of Glenelg–Knoydart established by Ramsay and Spring (1962) and the local stratigraphic sequences at Kinlochhourn. The recognition of thin slivers of Lewisian at Kinlochhourn and in Glen Shiel within the slide zone provided further evidence for the existence of a major tectonic break.

The Sgurr Beag Slide is a NNE-trending, steeply eastward dipping planar or slightly curved structure which along its trace in the Kintail district is marked by a sharp west-to-east change from fine-grained psammites or semipelites of the Morar Division to the coarse-grained gneissose psammites and pelites of the western part of the Glenfinnan Division. In Glen Shiel, Lewisian inliers occur in an narrow, elongated zone 50–100 m east of the boundary between the calcsilicate-bearing non-gneissose psammitic rocks of the Morar Division and gneissose psammites of the Glenfinnan Division. The slide has been mapped at the contact between the gneissose psammite and calcsilicate-bearing rocks of the Morar Division although Rathbone and Harris (1979) place the slide along the western boundary at the Lewisian inliers. From the ridge west of Sgurr Beag [NG 998 109] northward into Glen Shiel rocks adjacent to the slide have a platy appearance and Rathbone and Harris (1979) have shown that, in a west-to-east traverse across the slide, there is evidence of increasing strain from about 750 m west of the zone of Lewisian pods, with the disappearance of cross-bedding, tightening of folds and the development of a consistent foliation parallel to the slide. Some of the psammite east of the Lewisian pods is also platy. Such fissile, platy rocks are also known on the limbs of early folds, such as fold 1, the Sgurr nan Eugallt Fold (Tanner, 1971).

North of Glen Shiel, the Sgurr Beag Slide is well exposed in the bed of the Allt an Fhraoch Choire, at the site of a footbridge [026 168], not far above its junction with the Allt Granda. Here northward-trending, almost vertical beds of thinly flaggy non-gneissose micaceous psammite and semipelite are succeeded eastwards by gneissose semipelite and psammite with numerous quartzofeldspathic lits, the transition between the two rock groups being over about 10 m.

In Glen Shiel the Lewisian inliers in the Sgurr Beag Slide zone have a tectonic contact with the rocks of the Glenfinnan Division. Further north, in central Ross-shire, Tanner et al. (1970) suggest that the Scardroy Lewisian, which lies above the Sgurr Beag Slide at the same structural level as the Lewisian inliers in Glen Shiel, retains the original basement/cover relationship and that the Glenfinnan Division may have been deposited on a Lewisian basement.

Tanner et al. (1970) and Tanner (1971) concluded that the Sgurr Beag Slide is overprinted by D3$_M$ folds and that movement along the slide zone is broadly synchronous with the D2$_M$ episode of deformation; slide movement ceased before the cessation of D2$_M$ folding. Hence, the slide is deformed by folds associated with the still evolving Sgurr nan Eugalt D2$_M$ fold (fold 1, Figure 16). Powell et al. (1981) consider that movement along the slide was synchronous with a major fold episode and is probably an early Caledonian feature folded by at least two further phases of folding.

The amount of displacement along the Sgurr Beag Slide has not been established. The largely conformable attitude of the slide and the absence of marker horizons makes this very difficult to determine. Lambert et al. (1979), on the basis of displacement of metamorphic zones, proposed a movement along the slide of some 25 km.

## OTHER SLIDES

A number of slides occur elsewhere in the Kintail district south of the Strathconon Fault. In the area about 1 km NE of Kinloch Hourn the contact between subdivisions 2a and 2b (Figure 15) is a tectonic break which truncates lithological banding. Tanner (1971) reported the semipelite at the junction of these two subdivisions to be fissile and platy in places, suggesting the possible presence of a slide. Such a slide may mark the northward continuation of the Knoydart Slide (Powell, 1974). Further west the presence of hornblendic rocks of Lewisian type [NG 925 100] suggests that other slides may exist within the Morar Division rocks in this part of the map area, analogous to those in this Division northwest of the Strathconon Fault (Figure 11).

The contact between Area 4 and the Morar Division rocks of Area 5 is considered to be a slide zone. Morar Division rocks of the type area in Morar are underlain by the thin Basal Pelite rather than by a thick assemblage of gneissose Moine rocks, partly of Glenfinnan aspect, interleaved with Lewisian. West of Glen Shiel, Simony (1963, 1973) suggested that the slide zone between Areas 4 and 5 developed on the limb of a major $D2_M$ fold which refolds earlier Moine and Lewisian fold intercalations and proposed the slide to be an extension of the Sgurr Beag Slide. If his correlation of the bounding slide of Area 4 with the Sgurr Beag Slide is correct then it implies all the Moine rocks of Area 4 are correlatable with the Glenfinnan Division, although some of the psammites are lithologically similar to those of the Morar Division.

FIVE

# Pre-Caledonian, Caledonian and Post-Caledonian igneous rocks

## PRE-CALEDONIAN IGNEOUS ROCKS

Ten bodies of hornblende-schist have been mapped, all located within rocks of the Glenfinnan Division south-east of the Strathconon Fault. They vary in thickness from 0.3 m to 4.0 m and their length may extend up to several tens of metres. All are concordant with the lithological banding in the surrounding Moine rocks and have sharp, distinct contacts. In hand specimen the hornblende-schist is a black foliated rock, the foliation being defined by laminae alternately rich in hornblende and quartz and feldspar. The hornblende-schists are composed chiefly of green hornblende and quartz. Plagioclase (oligoclase) is equal in abundance with hornblende in some of the bodies, but is subsidiary or almost absent in others. Garnet is a common minor constituent and small amounts of sphene and iron oxide also occur. Biotite is sometimes present and partly replaces hornblende in a few specimens.

The relationship of the hornblende-schist bodies to fold structures and the Caledonian minor intrusions cannot be determined from the schist bodies located, but on the adjacent Sheet 72E similar hornblende-schist bodies are cut by the Caledonian regional pegmatites and are folded by $D2_M$ structures.

The hornblende-schist bodies are interpreted as metamorphosed minor intrusions in which all trace of the original mineralogy and texture has been destroyed by intense metamorphism and recrystallisation.

## CALEDONIAN AND POST-CALEDONIAN IGNEOUS ROCKS

### Introduction

The Caledonian and Post-Caledonian intrusions of the Kintail district belong to several distinct suites. Most of the dykes belong to swarms that extend beyond the limits of Sheet 72W. The age relations between the different suites have been firmly established and are shown in Table 12; their distribution is shown diagrammatically on Figure 17.

**Table 12** Classification and age relations between igneous suites intrusive into the Moine of Sheet 72W.

| Age | Rock type | Age relations | |
|---|---|---|---|
| Tertiary | Dolerite and basalt | Cut Ratagain Plutonic Complex and Strathconon Fault | |
| Permo-Carboniferous | Camptonite, camptonitic basalt, monchiquite | Cut Ratagain Plutonic Complex and Strathconon Fault | |
| Lower Devonian | Acid porphyrite, felsite, lamprophyre. Microdiorite of Ratagain | Cut Ratagain Plutonic Complex, displaced by Strathconon Fault. Cuts Ratagain Plutonic Complex, cut by lamprophyre | Post-Caledonian |
| | Ratagain Plutonic Complex (425 ± 3 Ma) | Spatially related to unmetamorphosed microdiorite and acid porphyrite. Displaced by Strathconon Fault | |
| Siluro-Ordovician | Felsic porphyrite, microdiorite, appinite | Cuts Cluanie Granodiorite (Sheet 72E) | Late to Post-Caledonian |
| | Early felsic porphyrite | Cut by Cluanie Granodiorite (425 ± 4 Ma) (Sheet 72E) | |
| | Pegmatite and aplite | Late stage transgressive bodies occurring on a regional scale | Caledonian and Pre-Caledonian |
| | Amphibolite and hornblende-schist | Pre-$D2_M$ minor intrusions in the Moine | Pre-Caledonian |

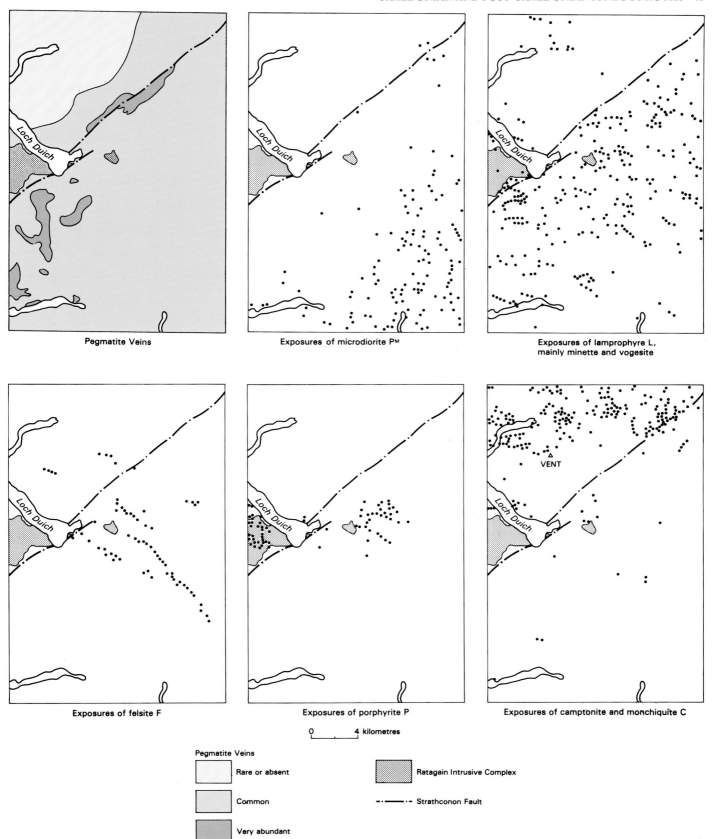

**Figure 17** Distribution of igneous suites.

The Silurian and Lower Devonian (late Caledonian) minor intrusions have been divided into two main groups (Table 12). The early microdiorite suite of felsic porphyrites, microdiorites and appinites, although individually small, are present in large numbers in the eastern part of the area where they constitute the north-western margin of a very extensive dyke swarm stretching southwards to the Sound of Mull (Smith, 1979). Many members of the suite are foliated and show granoblastic textures, and folded and garnet-bearing varieties are known from south of Kintail. A regional variation in the degree of deformation and recrystallisation exhibited by the intrusions has been attributed by Dearnley (1967) to a late Caledonian phase of regional metamorphism, the metamorphic grade decreasing towards the west. No cross-cutting relationships have been established with the Ratagain Plutonic complex, but as the complex and its associated minor intrusions are non-metamorphic it is thought to postdate the intrusions of the early Silurian microdiorite suite.

The younger Lower Devonian suite of acid porphyrite, felsite, lamprophyre and microdiorite dykes are spatially related to the Ratagain Plutonic Complex, the first two types being part of a narrow, well-defined swarm trending NW–SE. The lamprophyres, although also occurring as a similarly oriented swarm to the north-west of Ratagain, are much more widely distributed and in the Kintail area cut members of the older Silurian and Lower Devonian microdiorite suite.

The Tertiary basalt and Permo-Carboniferous camptonite-monchiquite suites are not always readily separable in the field. The former are rare and are marginal representatives of the north-west-trending Skye dyke swarm which crosses the Glenelg district, while the camptonite-monchiquite dykes are part of a major east–west-trending swarm, part of which has been traced in the north of the Kintail district (Figure 17).

## Pegmatite and aplite

Transgressive veins of granitic pegmatite, some possibly of pre-Caledonian age, are common in most parts of the Moine. In a few places they are sufficiently abundant to form ramifying networks in the metamorphic rocks. (The mainly concordant veins and lits related migmatisation are not included in this account).

North-north-east from Loch Hourn there are large areas within which pegmatite veins are abundant and where they can constitute up to 50 per cent of the exposed rock (Figure 17a). The pegmatites vary in thickness from a few centimetres to several metres and rarely tens of metres and although generally parallel-sided they ramify and coalesce, behaving in a manner described by C T Clough in his field notes as 'rambling'. Most of the pegmatites consist of quartz and feldspar with sparse mica, usually muscovite, and subsidiary biotite. Books of mica up to and occasionally a little larger than $3 \times 3 \times 1.5$ cm have been recorded. The large feldspars are commonly, but not invariably, microcline-microperthite, while quartz and oligoclase form finer-grained granular aggregates. Mica tends to be more prominent where the country rock is pelite, but neither the proportion nor the size of the books is large enough to be of possible

economic significance. No occurrences of rare minerals have been recorded.

Although the general distribution of the pegmatite vein complexes seems to be unrelated to the host rock geology, it has been noted that especially thick pegmatite bodies sometimes lie at the contact between contrasting rock types. For example, to the south of the Dubh Lochain [NG 890 090] the contact between gneissose siliceous psammite and feldspathic pelitic schists is marked in places by pegmatite bodies some 20–30 m across. A zone of pegmatites follows a pelitic band located about 400 m north-west of the summit of Sgurr Thionail [NG 984 088], and a plexus of aplite veins associated with pegmatite occurs on the hillside south of Kinlochhourn [NG 952 063].

Elsewhere, notably in Upper Glen Lichd, occasional veins of pegmatite, locally as much as 10 m thick, have been recorded, and a pegmatite mass about 800 m long and up to 150 m across occurs on A'Mhuing [NG 950 160], above Glen Shiel.

Locally within the Glenfinnan Division pelitic schists are converted in varying degrees to trondhjemitic pegmatites (cf. Summary of Progress of Geological Survey of Great Britain for 1962, p.52). Such trondhjemitic bodies are of irregular form and have diffuse margins. Most occur in a poorly defined zone, a kilometre or so wide, which extends from the Kinlochhourn Fault NNE through Sgurr a'Mhaoraich [NG 984 066] to Sgurr Beag [NG 997 109]. One mass of replacive pegmatite has been displaced dextrally more than 1 km by the fault (published sheet 72W). The trondhjemitic pegmatites usually display a foliation which is defined by a parallelism of fairly large flakes of mica. Locally, rafts of country rock, relatively unaltered, occur within the bodies. The few thin sections examined suggest that these mainly replacive pegmatites lack potash feldspar, consisting primarily of quartz and oligoclase and, like the parent schists, contain both muscovite and biotite.

## Early felsic porphyrite

Only a few examples of this suite have been mapped near the east margin of the sheet north of Glen Shiel. They are leucocratic to mesocratic rocks distinguished in hand specimen from the later felsic porphyrites by the larger size and greater proportion of the feldspar phenocrysts. The field relationships have been firmly established on the adjoining Sheet 72E. No member of the suite cuts the Cluanie Granodiorite, though they are spatially associated with it. Sheets of early felsic porphyrite are cut by pegmatite and aplite veins extending from the granodiorite and blocks of porphyrite are found within the microdiorite matrix of the Ceannacroc breccias. The early felsic porphyrites thus predate both the microdiorite suite and the Cluanie Granodiorite, but the close association with the latter indicates a genetic relationship (Smith, 1979).

Petrographically the early felsic porphyrites are porphyritic microgranodiorites. They are commonly weakly schistose and in thin section show some degree of recrystallisation. The phenocrysts, which are only slightly affected by this recrystallisation, are chiefly oscillatory-zoned albite-oligoclase up to 5 mm across accompanied by smaller and subsidiary green hornblende and biotite. The latter minerals occur also in the granoblastic groundmass which is composed mainly of plagioclase with subsidiary quartz. Sphene is a common accessory mineral.

## Microdiorite suite

### GENERAL

The members of this suite have been subdivided for purposes of field classification into felsic porphyrite, leucomicrodiorite (quartz microdiorite), microdiorite, melamicrodiorite, leucoappinite and appinite. In a regional context complete transitions in petrographic characteristics can be found between adjacent members of the above-listed rock types. Furthermore, sheets of appinite grading into melamicrodiorite and microdiorite, and net-veined by leucomicrodiorite, are not uncommon. In view of these associations age relations within the suite may have little real significance. Nevertheless there is some evidence from consistent cross-cutting relationships to indicate that the felsic porphyrites postdate the melamicrodiorites.

The intrusions of this suite are largely confined to the eastern half of the Kintail sheet area. A boundary which marks the western limit of appinites and microdiorites (with a few exceptions, mainly on the north side of Loch Hourn) runs from close to the north-east corner of the area in a south-westerly direction to near Kinlochourn. The western boundary of felsic porphyrites lies 4–5 km further to the east.

Most of the intrusions occur as sheets inclined to the east or south-east at less than 50°. A minority are vertical or dip north-west. The average width is 1 m with the majority lying in the range 0.3–2.0 m. A few exceptions reach 3–5 m in thickness. The appinites tend to occur as thicker sheets or small bosses up to 30 m across. Numerically the microdiorites constitute the most important group, 140 intrusions of this type having been mapped compared with 13 appinites (including 5 bodies of leucoappinite in the north-east corner of the map), and 8 felsic porphyrites.

An internal foliation and/or lineation is present in some members of each rock type, especially in the microdiorites, of which about one third are foliated. The foliation, which usually has the form of a closely spaced cleavage marked by a preferred orientation of biotite and/or hornblende, may be confined to the margins of the intrusion in which case it is normally parallel to the walls, or may extend across the body in a sigmoidal fashion with a maximum dip that is consistently steeper than that of the intrusion. The mapped intrusions in the Kintail district are not folded and the internal fabric appears to be the result of simple shear deformation, the intrusions behaving as small shear zones with a sinistral displacement. Where a lineation is present in sheets dipping south-east it invariably plunges steeply downwards towards the south-east or SSE.

### APPINITE

In appearance the appinites are medium- to coarse-grained dark green or black rocks, often with irregular patches and veins of felsic material. Petrographically they are best described as mafic diorites composed essentially of green hornblende and brown biotite, rarely accompanied by pyroxene, together with oligoclase. Variable, but usually small, amounts of potash feldspar and quartz also occur. Characteristic features are the presence of dark brown densely schillerised patches within the pale green hornblende plates and the partial replacement of the hornblende by flakes of biotite. The leucoappinites are quartz-diorites and granodiorites in which subsidiary hornblende and biotite are poikilitically enclosed in large (3 mm) plagioclase crystals which are accompanied by minor quartz and K-feldspar. They are locally cut by leucomicrodiorite sheets, for instance at a locality [NH 055 293], 700 m NW of Loch an Droma.

### MICRODIORITE

Of 70 thin sections cut from the microdiorites, 27 are foliated, 27 have textures with varying degrees of recrystallisation and 16 show original unmodified igneous textures. The microdiorites are all composed essentially of plagioclase, quartz and potash-feldspar with varying amounts of hornblende and/or biotite and accessory sphene, opaque oxide and apatite. Epidote, chlorite and carbonate are also present in some rocks. Differences in the relative abundance of the principal minerals constitute a continuous series from medium-grained mafic microdiorite rich in hornblende, through microdiorite and leucomicrodiorite, to microgranodiorite in which the grain size is usually greater and significant amounts of quartz and potash feldspar are present. Porphyritic varieties of each type occur with phenocrysts of plagioclase and/or hornblende. Phenocrysts are rare in the more mafic members but plagioclase phenocrysts increase in number in the leucomicrodiorites and microgranodiorites as the composition approaches that of the felsic porphyrites. In all but the most mafic microdiorites, the most abundant mineral constituent is a zoned plagioclase occurring as euhedral or subhedral tabular crystals with turbid cores ranging in composition from andesine in the microdiorites to calcic oligoclase in the microgranodiorites. Quartz and untwinned potash feldspar occur interstitially. Hornblende is usually the dominant ferromagnesian mineral, though in some cases it is exceeded by biotite, especially at the more acidic end of the group. The hornblende is typically green in colour and often shows the same features seen in the appinites, that is, brown-coloured cores with parallel rods of opaque iron oxide lying across the length of the hornblende crystal, and partial replacement by reddish brown biotite.

A majority of the slices show evidence of partial granulation and recrystallisation culminating in the foliated intrusions, some of which are thoroughly schistose and granoblastic. An initial stage is marked by the presence of widely spaced biotite-rich laminae accompanied by a slight granulation of interstitial quartz and potash feldspar. At a more advanced stage, groundmass plagioclase also becomes partially recrystallised into small equant grains although phenocrysts tend to be more resistant and survive as eyes around which the foliation is deflected. The hornblende crystals become either aligned in the foliation planes or more granular and equidimensional. Lenticular aggregations appear to represent the sites of former phenocrysts. The most strongly foliated examples have a penetrative schistosity of aligned biotite and hornblende and a distinct granoblastic texture in the quartzofeldspathic constituents which may also exhibit an elongation in the schistosity plane.

FELSIC PORPHYRITE

The felsic porphyrites are typically pale grey or whitish in colour with conspicuous phenocrysts of feldspar. Most can be classed as porphyritic microgranodiorites and in thin section all show some degree of recrystallisation. The dominant phenocryst is oscillatory-zoned albite-oliglase up to 4 mm across. Dark brown biotite occurs as large single crystals or elongate spindle-shaped aggregates, while hornblende, when present, forms clear bright green prisms up to 2 mm in length. Biotite and hornblende may both appear in the fine-grained groundmass but the dominant constituents are quartz, plagioclase and potash feldspar with a typically equigranular granoblastic texture. In one foliated example some of the plagioclase phenocrysts show incipient marginal granulation, and patches of coarser groundmass, rich in potash feldspar grains with 120° triple junctions, occupy 'shadow zones' between adjacent phenocrysts.

No systematic distribution of degree of granulation or schistosity is evident in the Kintail area although there is a tendency for unmodified igneous microdiorites to be more common north of Glen Shiel. Of the six intrusions which occur further west, on the north side of Loch Hourn, three show igneous textures and three are foliated sheets.

The possibility must be considered that the acid porphyrites of Ratagain (p.57) are the nonmetamorphic equivalents of the felsic porphyrites in eastern Glen Shiel. Petrographically the two types are similar, especially in their characteristic oscillatory-zoned plagioclase phenocrysts. The marked difference in mode of occurrence and orientation between the groups could be interpreted as being due to differing environmental conditions during the time of intrusion. Three factors, however, support the view that they belong to separate suites of different age.

i) The felsites and acid porphyrites are intimately related and dykes of felsite cross the area of partially recrystallised felsic porphyrites without themselves showing any effects.

ii) The lamprophyres are certainly younger than the felsic porphyrites and several examples are known of acid porphyrites cutting lamprophyre. However, two cases of lamprophyre cutting felsite have also been recorded perhaps indicating overlap of the periods of intrusion.

iii) A single isolated sheet of felsic porphyrite on Sgurr na Carnach [NG 973 160], well to the west of the other members of this group, shows slight groundmass recrystallisation, while felsites and porphyrites a short distance to the north are unaffected. Although this evidence might suggest a rapid falling-off westwards of metamorphic grade it seems unlikely that the gradient could have been sufficiently steep to have made no imprint on the nearby felsites and porphyrites.

## Dyke-like body of granodiorite

A small unfoliated, post-tectonic granodiorite body crops out in the Allt a'Chaoruinn Bhig, 700 m north of Cluanie Inn [NH 076 127]. The rock is a pale pink equigranular granodiorite with very subsidiary biotite and hornblende. In the stream the southern edge of the intrusion is bounded by schist with granodiorite veins forming a zone about 100 m wide, in contrast to the northern edge which is a sharp junction with no disruption of the adjacent country rock. The granodiorite is also exposed in a gully to the west of the main stream where it forms a vertical dyke-like body about 30 m wide which appears to thin and die out westwards. Though the granodiorite can probably be classed with the Caledonian igenous rocks its relationship to the other suites of this age is not known.

## Ratagain Plutonic Complex

(*Contribution by D H W Hutton,*[1] *W E Stephens,*[2] *B Yardley,*[3] *M McErlean*[1] *and A N Halliday*[4]).

The Ratagain complex comprises principally diorites and quartz monzonites but minor variants range from melanocratic rocks belonging to the appinite suite through syenites to true granites. The whole complex is cut by late minor intrusives (Table 12). The pluton is important in the context of Caledonian magmatism in that it represents a link, or transition, between the calcalkaline characteristics of the vast majority of the 'Newer Granites' of Scotland and the alkaline characteristics of contemporaneous magmatism in the North-west Highlands, including the syenitic intrusions of Assynt. The complex has some notable compositional characteristics, especially in the remarkably high abundances of some trace elements, particularly Sr, Ba and light rare earth elements.

The complex was first described in the Geological Survey Memoir for Sheet 71 (Peach et al., 1910) and a more comprehensive petrological investigation was published by Nicholls (1951a, b). These authors established the principal units of the complex and their general petrological characteristics. Geochronological studies indicate that the pluton was emplaced at 425 ± 3 Ma (U-Pb determination on baddeleyite from a pyroxene mica diorite by Rogers and Dunning, 1991), more or less coeval with the Assynt alkaline suite and the Ben Loyal syenite (van Breemen et al., 1979, Halliday et al., 1987). The U-Pb age determination on a zircon from the quartz monzonite by Aftalion et al. (1984) yielded an unrealistically young age of about 365 Ma which the authors interpreted as reflecting some loss of radiogenic Pb from the zircons. The Rb-Sr biotite-feldspar and biotite-whole rock isochron age of 415 ± 5 Ma determined by Turnell (1985) was adjusted to 419 ± 3 Ma by Thirlwall (1988) and probably reflects fairly rapid cooling of the complex.

The Ratagain complex has an exposed outcrop of some 17 km$^2$ with a presumed extension under Loch Duich. Only the eastern part of the complex occurs in the area of Sheet 72W, but for convenience the whole complex is described in this account. Recent extensive road cuttings associated with forestry activities and with improvements to the Glenelg

1 Department of Geological Sciences, University of Durham, Durham DH1 3LE
2 Department of Geography and Geology, University of St Andrews, Fife KY16 9ST
3 Department of Earth Sciences, The University, Leeds LS2 9JT
4 Scottish Universities Research and Reactor Centre, East Kilbride, Glasgow G75 0QU.

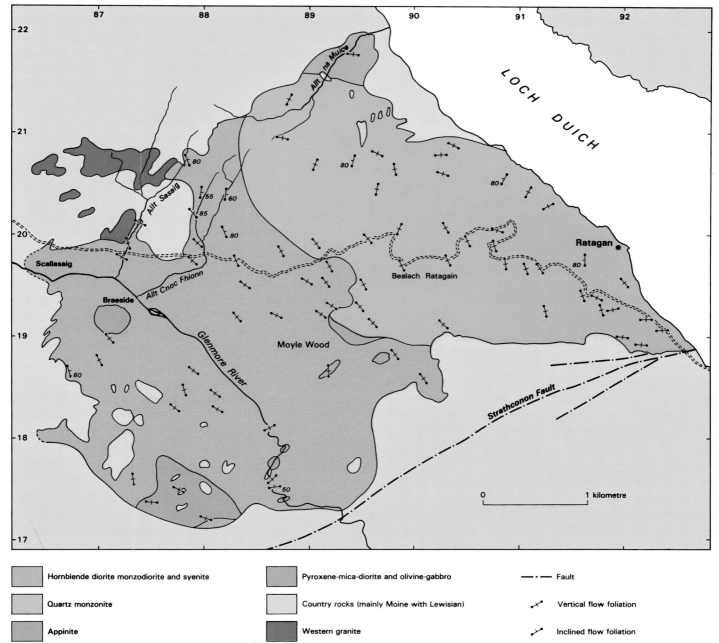

**Figure 18**  Summary petrological map of the Ratagain igneous complex.

road over Mam Ratagan have created new exposures, providing information not available to earlier workers. Data from a complete remapping of the complex and from the Geological Survey field maps of Clough (Peach et al., 1910) have been combined to produce a new map of the complex (Figure 18). This map has significant differences from the published map of Nicholls (1951a) and the 1:50 000 Sheet 72W, differences which relate mainly to the 'Western Granite' of Sheet 71E, the outcrop distribution of the appinites, the diorite–quartz monzonite contact, and the adopted petrological nomenclature. The petrological members of the complex are defined using the IUGS classification (Streckeisen, 1976).

The pluton was emplaced in Moine metasediments and Lewisian units of the Glenelg inlier and is located some 4.5 km east of the trace of the Moine Thrust (Figure 2). Emplacement of the pluton took place at about 425 Ma during the later stages of movement of the Moine Thrust system (Halliday et al., 1987). The pluton is cut by the Strathconon Fault and the granitic body in Glen Licht [NG 970 200], south-east of the fault, may be part of the Ratagain complex (Dhonau, 1964). If such a correlation is correct it implies a sinistral displacement by the Strathconon Fault of at least 6 km.

The outer contacts of the pluton are rarely exposed. However, in the Allt Sasaig [NG 874 202], Allt na Muice

[NG 896 220] and Glenmore river [NG 865 194] the contact can be seen to be gently dipping, which is consistent with the outcrop pattern in the north, west and south of the pluton where the contact is subparallel to the contours of the valleys. Only in the south-east of the pluton is the contact nearly vertical. Where the contact is steep thermal metamorphic effects are restricted to narrow zones not more than 5 m wide, with cordierite hornfelses and evidence of local anatexis occurring at the diorite–Moine psammite contact. No obvious alteration is seen in the rocks in contact with the quartz monzonite. In the western part of the complex, north of the Glenmore River, the present topographic surface appears to be nearly parallel to the roof of the diorite and only a short distance below it. The Western Granite mapped by Clough (Peach et al., 1910) was described by Nicholls (1951a) as consisting of hornblende-biotite granite, partly porphyritic and grading into granodiorite, with both earlier and later quartzofeldspathic veining. The area of the Western Granite consists dominantly of Moine metasediments invaded by both diorite and granite in complex relationships. Nicholls (1951a) interpreted the Western Granite as the first phase of the Ratagain complex but the petrogenetic relationships are tenuous and it is possible that it is not related to the development of the main diorite-monzonite complex.

The field evidence indicates that the roof contact of the diorite dips gently westwards, presumably underlying the Western Granite at shallow depth. The gravity anomalies on the Bouguer Gravity Anomaly Map (1:250 000 Series, 1976) and magnetic anomaly data on the Aeromagnetic Anomaly Map (1:250 000 Series, 1978) suggest that beyond the roof zone the pluton contacts dip steeply indicating that the overall form is one of a flat-topped pluton with steep sides. The contacts are invariably sharp and cross-cut structures in the country rocks.

The main rock types of the complex are shown on Figure 18 and are:

### Hornblende diorite, monzodiorite and syenite

The hornblende diorite is particularly variable and heterogeneous and has numerous inclusions, 0.01–0.2 m in size, of amphibole-rich ('appinite' and meladiorite) material scattered through the body. In the field the usual rock type seen is medium grained but the diorite grades from fine to coarse grained although locally sharp internal boundaries between different facies have been observed as, for example, in the Glenmore River. Petrographically, the most common rock is a hornblende-biotite-diorite with accessory apatite, titanite and celestine. Nicholls (1951a) recorded a large area of syenite separating the diorite from the quartz monzonite. The present mapping of the same area identified diorites with a pink alkali feldspar-rich matrix, modally best described as monzodiorites, as well as syenite. The syenite is considered not to be an extensive and discrete mappable unit but rather a local facies within the diorite that has gradational contacts with both the diorite and monzodiorite. The syenite is quartz-bearing locally (the nordmarkite of Nicholls, 1951a), for example on the north side of the Glenelg road east of Allt Cnoc Fhionn, and typically contains clinopyroxene, amphibole, alkali felspar and plagioclase as well as quartz and accessory titanite.

### Pyroxene mica diorite and olivine gabbro

Locally the diorite contains pyroxene rather than amphibole; examples of this rock type crop out in the Glenmore River, and at Braeside. The rock is typically a fine- to medium-grained diorite with clinopyroxene and biotite set in a matrix of andesine with minor amounts of opaque minerals. Olivine gabbro, which geochemically represents the least evolved member of the complex, has been recognised associated with pyroxene mica diorite and hornblende diorite near the western outer contact in outcrops south of Braeside. The gabbro contains rather altered olivine, clinopyroxene with plagioclase and subordinate alkali feldspar. Quench textures from specimens adjacent to a metasedimentary xenolith indicate the pluton probably had a chilled margin of this olivine gabbro which was later incorporated in the marginal parts of the main amphibole diorite.

### Quartz monzonite

The quartz monzonite (equivalent to the adamellite as described by Nicholls, 1951a) occupies the core of the pluton and is normally pink in appearance. In the west and northeast the quartz monzonite was emplaced in the dioritic margin of the pluton while in the south and north the quartz monzonite is in contact with country rocks. The eastern margin is obscured by Loch Duich. The contact with the diorite is a zone some 200 m wide, well exposed in the Ratagain–Glenelg road cuttings, in which quartz monzonite sheets intrude the diorite in a steeply inclined contact zone. The quartz monzonite normally contains both biotite and hornblende and the total mafic mineral content is variable, tending to be higher towards the contact with the diorites. Near this contact there is evidence of contamination of the quartz monzonite by amphibole-rich material, shown by the presence of appinitic and dioritic inclusions of varying size, down to single discrete amphibole crystals. In the direction away from the contact with the diorite there is a gradual increase in the quartz content and the rock becomes granitic in composition in the centre of the quartz monzonite. Whether this compositional change is a lateral or concentric petrological zoning is not clear as Loch Duich obscures the eastern margin of the complex.

### Appinite suite

Intrusions of this suite occur as discrete pipes and as abundantly distributed enclaves in both the diorite and quartz monzonite throughout most of the outer portion of the pluton. In terms of the current IUGS petrological nomenclature the appinites of this suite are meladiorites, melamonzonites and melasyenites. The mafic mineralogy consists of hornblende, biotite and occasionally pyroxene with a total mafic modal abundance of up to 90 per cent, and the plagioclase to alkali feldspar ratio in the groundmass is highly variable. Calcite, apatite and celestine are common accessory minerals. The best exposures of hornblende-rich appinite occur in the Glenmore River and in exposures along the forestry roads in Moyle Wood. One such outcrop, at locality [NG 897 189], consists of pillow-like masses, 0.1–0.5 m in size, of melamonzonite with the long axes of the 'pillows' aligned vertically in a matrix of pink monzonite to form a vertical pipe-like structure. At least one of the appinite-like bodies in the Glenmore River was considered by Nicholls (1951b) to be a skarn.

### Late veins

The quartz monzonite is cut by quartz-fluorite-calcite veins near to the Strathconon Fault system (Alderton, 1988). The ore mineralogy of these veins includes pyrite, chalcopyrite, galena and sphalerite with minor hessite and electrum; gold occurs in the electrum and silver in the galena (Alderton 1986, 1988). The high temperatures indicated by fluid inclusions and the enrichment of these fluids in Sr and Ba suggests a close genetic link between this mineralisation and the magmatism.

Major oxide and selected trace element abundances of representative samples of the main rock types in the Ratagain complex are presented in Table 13. These indicate that it is enriched in alkalies (especially $Na_2O$) when compared with the entire 'Newer Granite' province. The complex as a whole describes a smooth trend on a $Na_2O + K_2O$: $FeO + Fe_2O_3$: MgO plot, typical of calcalkaline igneous series (Stephens and Halliday, 1984, Halliday and Stephens, 1984). Trace element studies by Halliday et al. (1984) indicate notably high values of Sr (typically 2000–5000 ppm in diorites reflecting the presence of primary celestine), Ba (up to 6000 ppm in syenitic facies rocks), and Ce (up to 500 ppm in diorites indicating high titanite abundances). The early

gabbros and pyroxene mica diorites have general isotopic compositions of $(^{87}Sr/^{86}Sr)_{425}$~0.7058, $\epsilon Nd$~-4, $\delta^{18}O$~7‰; the amphibole diorites and quartz monzonites have general isotopic compositions of $(^{87}Sr/^{86}Sr)_{425}$~0.7052, $\epsilon Nd$~-13, $\delta^{18} = 7$-9‰; and in some appinites isotopic compositions of $(^{87}Sr/^{86}Sr)_{425}$~0.7058, $\epsilon Nd$~-7, $\delta^{18}O$~6-8‰ have been recorded (Halliday et al., 1984).

The earliest foliation is of magmatic type and is formed from the alignment of euhedral plagioclase feldspars and mafic clusters within a groundmass showing no deformation (pre-full crystallisation type in the system of Hutton, 1988). The planar fabric is steeply inclined and can be seen in places to have a subhorizontal linear component. The fabric directly under the gently inclined roof contacts has a strike direction of N–S or NW–SE in the northern and western parts of the pluton and in some places strikes directly towards the intrusive contact. There is a progressive anticlockwise rotation of the foliation to a NE–SW or E–W trend adjacent to the southern contact of the complex, and to the Strathconon Fault (Figure 18). In the southern part of the Glenmore River deformation of the microdiorite xenoliths in the diorites progressively increases towards the trace of the Strathconon Fault and annealed shears within the higher strain zones show clear evidence of sinistral displacement. The broad anticlockwise swing in foliation trend, the steep planar fabric, the subhorizontal lineation, the small annealed shears and the increase in strain southwards are all consistent

**Table 13** Analyses of samples representative of the Ratagain Plutonic Complex.

| Sample | D90 | Rat 36 | Rat 1/2 | Rat 3/1 | Rat 5/4 | Rat 35 |
|---|---|---|---|---|---|---|
| $SiO_2$ | 51.6 | 55.7 | 66.5 | 58.9 | 42.2 | 71.71 |
| $TiO_2$ | 1.26 | 1.08 | 0.46 | 0.85 | 3.15 | 0.35 |
| $Al_2O_3$ | 13.82 | 16.34 | 15.68 | 14.37 | 12.79 | 14.51 |
| $Fe_2O_3$ | 3.49 | 1.63 | 0.88 | 1.92 | 3.30 | 1.18 |
| FeO | 4.00 | 4.60 | 1.75 | 3.33 | 8.75 | 1.10 |
| MnO | 0.11 | 0.11 | 0.06 | 0.11 | 0.17 | 0.03 |
| MgO | 7.42 | 5.94 | 1.23 | 4.21 | 10.01 | 0.38 |
| CaO | 8.70 | 6.78 | 2.30 | 4.09 | 8.69 | 1.13 |
| $Na_2O$ | 3.2 | 3.9 | 5.5 | 5.7 | 1.9 | 4.0 |
| $K_2O$ | 3.48 | 3.12 | 4.18 | 4.68 | 4.28 | 5.48 |
| $P_2O_5$ | 1.07 | 0.77 | 0.27 | 0.68 | 2.11 | 0.14 |
| Loss | 0.3 | 0.4 | <0.05 | <0.05 | 1.8 | <0.05 |
| Nb | 14 | 10 | 23 | 24 | 27 | 16 |
| Zr | 328 | 223 | 228 | 431 | 200 | 263 |
| Y | 26 | 21 | 13 | 27 | 34 | 13 |
| Sr | 2520 | 2380 | 1770 | 1830 | 730 | 410 |
| Rb | 66 | 64 | 63 | 63 | 140 | 93 |
| Th | 20 | 17 | <2 | 2 | <2 | 17 |
| Pb | 21 | 9 | 14 | 14 | <3 | 14 |
| Zn | 56 | 93 | 43 | 79 | <2 | 29 |
| Cu | 101 | 2 | 4 | 32 | 149 | 5 |
| Ni | 192 | 144 | 17 | 75 | 208 | 7 |
| Cr | 341 | 255 | 17 | 131 | 309 | <1 |
| V | 147 | 131 | 40 | 112 | 399 | 30 |
| Ba | 1980 | 1860 | 1990 | 4270 | 2180 | 1130 |
| Ce | 384 | 222 | 115 | 299 | 200 | 178 |
| Total | 99.06 | 100.91 | 99.24 | 99.58 | 99.61 | 100.23 |
| Rock type | Olivine gabbro | Hornblende diorite | Quartz monzonite | Quartz syenite | Appinite | Western granite |
| NGR | NG 870 191 | NG 872 197 | NG 899 200 | NG 880 198 | NG 897 189 | NG 856 203 |

with a model in which the pluton was deformed by sinistral shear along the adjacent Strathconon Fault. This deformation occurred after the main magmatic units had been emplaced, but before they had completely crystallised.

A second main phase of deformation occurred after the major plutonic units had cooled and crystallised during and after the emplacement of regional dykes. The second deformation produced a network of NE–SW-trending low temperature brittle faults and mylonitic zones (see Nicholls, 1951a) which show only small sinistral displacements within the pluton. This later deformation may also be related to movement on the Strathconon Fault.

### Summary of the petrogenesis and geological history

The probable parental magmas for the gabbro and pyroxene mica diorite of the complex have primitive 'mantle-like' signatures in trace elements and isotopes, and the $\epsilon$Nd values are typical of contemporaneous mantle in northern Scotland (Thirlwall, 1982). The more evolved and hydrous members, the amphibole diorites, appinites, syenites and quartz monzonites, have features which have strong 'crustal' signatures (particularly the markedly negative $\epsilon$Nd values) indicating either distinct magma sources or, more probably, extensive crustal contamination of a mantle-derived parental magma. The emplacement of the pluton may be related to transtensional deformation adjacent to the Strathconon Fault. The evidence of extensive appinitic contamination of all members of the complex suggests that a major appinitic body developed early beneath the present exposure level and was intruded first by the diorite then by the quartz monzonite. It is probable that the diorite developed as several separate intrusions and development of syenitic facies within the amphibole diorite was related to in-situ evolutionary processes. The quartz monzonite is zoned inwardly towards granite. At a later stage appinite was intruded as a series of pipes mobilised by the quartz monzonitic magma. As the complex developed it was cut by dykes, both early microdiorites and later porphyrites and felsites (see section below) reflecting the evolving composition of the pluton. Late-stage lamprophyre dykes (minettes, see below) are displaced by the Strathconon Fault as are the earlier microdiorites, porphyrites and felsites and the fault was evidently active throughout the history of the pluton and controlled the injection of the late gold-bearing sulphide veins.

## Microdiorite of Ratagain

West of the Strathconon Fault zone and closely associated with the Ratagain Complex there occurs a small group of mafic minor intrusions whose relationship to the main suite of microdiorite further east is uncertain. They are medium- or fine-grained, grey or pale pink rocks occurring as dykes or steeply inclined sheets up to 3 m thick, although the average is about 1 m. Phenocrysts of hornblende and, less commonly, plagioclase are characteristically present. Direct evidence for age relations with other 'Caledonian' minor intrusions is confined to one example near Leacachan on the south-west shore of Loch Duich [NG 892 228] where a 1 m-wide pink microdiorite is cut by a thick minette.

Members of the suite cut all the plutonic phases of the Ratagain complex but are most common in the diorite.

Thin sections from these microdiorites are readily divisable into two groups. The first group consists of those which show normal, unmodified igneous textures. Most are porphyritic microdiorites but the more mafic members could perhaps be classed as spessartites while a few unusually rich in plagioclase show gradation towards the acid porphyrites. The relative proportion of potash feldspar to plagioclase is difficult to assess in many cases, but the group as a whole is probably richer in potash feldspar than the earlier microdiorite suite east of the Strathconon Fault and some would, perhaps, be better classed as micromonzonite. The most abundant phenocrysts are of euhedral green or brown hornblende, often with residual cores of colourless pyroxene partially or completely replaced by decussate aggregates of brown biotite. Individual large porphyritic plates of biotite also occur. Feldspar phenocrysts are much less common than amphibole and appear both as turbid, concentrically zoned, subhedral or euhedral single crystals, and as aggregates; some of the latter are highly corroded and may represent xenolith material from the Ratagain complex. The groundmass is commonly dominated by slightly cloudy, stumpy, zoned oligoclase laths with sericite cores, and small flakes of biotite. Hornblende is present in the groundmass of the more mafic examples, while potash feldspar, sometimes accompanied by a little quartz, forms an interstitial matrix in the more acidic types. Opaque oxide and apatite are ubiquitous accessories. In a minority of examples the feldspar occurs in sheaf-like aggregates engulfing a decussate biotite fabric, giving a lamprophyric look to the rock. A specimen of one of this type bears small ocelli containing a carbonate mineral and/or celestine.

The second group of thin sections is characterised by textures showing varying degrees of granularity and schistosity. Hornblende phenocrysts can be seen in all stages of crystallisation towards the development of clear, bright green equidimensional aggregates, lenticles and augen. In the groundmass brown biotite is abundant and usually accompanied by small amphiboles, while the plagioclase is clear and, especially in the schistose rocks, tends to be granoblastic. Quartz and potash feldspar are also generally present, the latter in some cases forming large poikiloblastic plates enclosing the other minerals of the groundmass.

No spatial distinction is evident between the two groups described above. Both types occur within a few feet of each other in the Glen More River at the southern end of the Ratagain complex. It is possible, therefore, that an extended period of intrusion is involved, the earlier dykes attaining their granular texture and schistosity prior to the emplacement of those with an igneous texture. The effects seen in the 'granular group' cannot be attributed to a simple thermal hornfelsing by the rocks of the Ratagain complex since most of them cut the major intrusion and three of the schistose dykes cut the youngest member — the quartz monzonite. It seems, therefore, that either the presumed earlier dykes were intruded while the complex and its immediate environment were still hot enough to cause an immediate recrystallisation accompanied by a local slight shearing movement, or they have been preferentially sheared and recrystallised by a more regional metamorphic event, later than, but in other respects similar to, that which affected the main microdiorite suite further to the east.

## Felsite and acid porphyrite

Although uncommon and confined to the northern part of the Kintail District, the dykes of this suite form a well-defined swarm centred on the Ratagain complex (Peach et al., 1919, p.87). They are best developed north-west of the Strathconon Fault where they cut all the members of the Ratagain complex. Another group, mainly felsites, occurs in an area extending from Ben Attow to near Cluanie Inn and is the faulted south-eastwards continuation of the swarm displaced by the Strathconon Fault. The orientation of the dykes changes from ESE on the north-west side of the fault to a south-east trend south-east of the fault.

The dykes vary in colour from pale pink or cream in the felsites to reddish brown in the porphyrites, and in thickness from 1 to 10 m with an average thickness of about 4 m. Feldspar phenocrysts are small and sparse or absent in the felsites, while in the porphyrites they are commonly so abundant that no matrix is visible in hand specimen and the rock resembles a microgranite. Most of the rocks in this suite could be classed as porphyritic microgranodiorite. The felsites show rare phenocrysts of bluish alkali feldspar up to 2.5 mm across, often with turbid edges, sericitised plagioclase of similar dimensions, and muscovite-sphene-iron oxide pseudomorphs after biotite. The groundmass is typical felsitic — fine-grained and quartzofeldspathic, with muscovite flakes and a little opaque oxide.

The feldspar phenocrysts in the porphyrites consist of oscillatory-zoned plagioclase about 2 mm long and are generally partially or completely sericitised. Perthitic alkali feldspar occurs as broad rims around the plagioclase and as individual plates up to 4 mm across enclosing small plagioclase laths.

In some thin sections a well-developed oscillatory zoning is present in the alkali feldspar phenocrysts which may also show a microcline-type cross-hatching. Quartz phenocrysts occur in about one third of the slices examined as sub-rounded corroded crystals up to 3 mm across. Of the ferro-magnesian minerals, biotite phenocrysts or chlorite-epidote-sphene pseudomorphs are always present, while hornblende is usually absent or represented by a few chlorite-carbonate pseudomorphs. Rarely, fresh hornblende phenocrysts exceed biotite in amount and occur as euhedral prisms up to 1.5 mm in length and colour-zoned from pale brown cores to olive-green rims. Accessory minerals include sphene, allanite and apatite. The groundmass of the acid porphyrites can be too fine grained and turbid for accurate determination of the constituent minerals but can usually be seen to consist of dominant plagioclase with subsidiary alkali feldspar and a little interstitial quartz. Variable amounts of biotite or secondary white mica in small flakes together with accessory apatite and opaque oxide complete the groundmass assemblage.

## Lamprophyre

The Lower Devonian lamprophyres occur as dykes usually varying in thickness from 0.3 to 6 m and are characterised by a conspicuous reddish brown colour. The majority form part of a large swarm trending NW–SE and extending beyond the limits of Sheet 72W. A smaller group, largely confined to the central-western part of the area, are aligned roughly parallel to the Strathconon fault system. They intrude the cataclastic rocks associated with early movements on the fault system, but the swarm as a whole is displaced in a sinistral sense by about 6 km (Smith, 1979).

Petrographically the majority of the dykes are normal pyroxene-minettes, being rich in corroded, colour-zoned phenocrysts of biotite and colourless or pale green clinopyroxene. They are identical to those described by Read et al. (1926) from the Strath Oykell region to the north and classed by him as augite-minettes. Carbonate or serpentinous pseudomorphs after olivine phenocrysts are not uncommon, while pale brown hornblende is also frequently present. In a small number of cases hornblende is the dominant ferromagnesian mineral and these rocks may be classed as vogesites. In most specimens of both types the fine- or medium-grained groundmass is dominantly feldspathic. Orthoclase and acid plagioclase are usually both present but their turbid and partly decomposed nature makes it difficult to determine their relative abundance. Quartz occurs interstitially, especially in the more felsic varieties, and also as xenocrysts. Apatite and magnetite are ubiquitous and abundant accessories.

## Camptonite-monchiquite suite

About 200 dykes of this suite have been recorded, the great majority in the northern quarter of the map. Those west of the Strathconon Fault comprise the Killilan swarm (Rock, 1983). A few dykes east of the fault could be a continuation of the Killilan swarm, but their trend (ENE–WSW) differs slightly from that of the Killilan swarm (east–west). Most of the dykes are less than a metre thick, though a few reach 3 m. One example is known of a monchiquite vent near Camas-luine [NG 9430 2730] (see below). A multiple dyke formed from a 1 m-thick minette sandwiched between camptonites 70 cm and 40 cm thick has been mapped in the Allt na Choire Chaoil, Killilan Forest [NH 0015 3183], an occurrence which is regarded as a fortuitous juxtaposition of unrelated rocks (Rock, 1983). Almost half of the dykes are classified as camptonite and camptonitic-basalt, a fifth as basalt and a tenth as monchiquite and camptonitic-monchiquite. A few are pyroxenitic or picritic. Dykes of the suite cut both the Ratagain complex and the Strathconon Fault system. The camptonite-monchiquite dyke swarm of Morar, which is separated from but otherwise similar to the Killilan swarm, has been radiometrically dated to about 325 Ma, that is to the Viséan stage (Baxter and Mitchell, 1984).

In the field the camptonites and camptonitic basalts are grey, fine-grained to aphanitic rocks, often with xenocrysts of pyroxene or anorthoclase and scattered leucocratic ocelli with kaersutite or biotite needles. Some dykes carry xenoliths of country rock and ultramafic rocks. The monchiquites contain analcime or glass and feldspar is either absent or present only in small amounts.

The monchiquite vent near Camas-luine is some 200 m long and 15 m wide and is interpreted as an exploded agglomerate dyke (Rock, 1983, Table 1). It contains (a) xenoliths of local country rock, including pelite, (b) megacrysts of carbonated and silicified spinel, lherzolite and clinopyroxene and (c) fragments of magnetite/apatite. A dyke by the roadside near Eilean Donan [NG 884 258], on the adjacent Sheet 71E, includes numerous xenoliths of Lewisian gneiss and amphibolite as well as siliceous schists of indeterminate provenance. (P Aspey, personal communication). There are also large megacrysts of clinopyroxene, kaersutitic amphibole, biotite and magnetite as well as clinopyroxene-biotite rock, clinopyroxene-biotite-kaersutite rock, and fragments of magnetite and apatite.

## Basalt and dolerite of Permo-Carboniferous or Tertiary age

A total of four dykes, of which none can be traced for any distance, has been mapped in the west central part of the area. The dykes are of variable trend and range in thickness from 1 to 2 m. Three are typical olivine-dolerites one of which cuts the fault rock of the Strathconon Fault system. One unusual type is an olivine-free hypersthene-basalt with a sparse glassy mesostasis, probably a tholeiite of Tertiary age.

# SIX

# Sodic metasomatite

Small outcrops of rock composed of albite, sodic amphibole, sodic pyroxene, actinolite and sphene, with baryte as an occasional accessory mineral, form clusters of occurrences crossing Loch Hourn (and in the nearby Carnach valley at the head of Loch Nevis [NG 888 004] on Sheet 62W) and in areas between Glen Elchaig and Loch Duich (published sheet 72W). The rocks form lenticular bodies and irregular patches of replacement which either cross-cut the country rocks (psammite with subsidiary semipelite) or merge with them.

In the Loch Hourn area Tanner and Tobisch (1972) mapped some 74 bodies. They subdivided the occurrences as follows:

Type I   Dykes, bosses and lenses of albite-pyroxene-hornblende rock which are discordant to the bedding foliation of the country rocks.

Type II   Massive bodies of albite rock which contain scattered porphyroblasts of pyroxene and amphibole.

Type III   Breccia of albitised country rock set in a matrix of pyroxene, albite and quartz, e.g. [NG 901 045].

Type IV   Cross-cutting alkali pegmatites which cause albitisation of the adjacent country rock and the local development of pyroxene and hornblende, e.g. [NG 983 073].

The Type I rocks are commonly crudely foliated and are composed mainly of albite with large crystals of sodic amphibole and sodic pyroxene. The foliation may be at an angle to that of the country rock or may be parallel to it. In the latter case the foliation is sometimes clearly mimetic, the original minor folds having been preserved during the metasomatic replacement of quartz, oligoclase, K-feldspar and micas by albite, sodic amphibole and sodic pyroxene. A good example is the isolated occurrence of sodic rocks on the north side of Loch Quoich [NG 998 035] (Sheet 62W), which is a partly concordant body some 180 m long and 6 m wide. On the north side of Loch Hourn [NG 899 071] another example of crudely foliated rock is marginal to a sheet-like body of dark green schistose rock 3 m wide which occupies an eastward-dipping joint. This is composed essentially of sodic pyroxene, albite and actinolite together with biotite, quartz and baryte. The schistosity is accompanied by a strong lineation in the ferromagnesian minerals and the feldspars are granulated and partly recrystallised. Type II rocks are exemplified on the south shore of Loch Hourn [NG 898 065] where an area of psammite about 90 m across is patchily metasomatised to a rock composed almost entirely of plagioclase. Thin sections show this to be andesine, but albite has been reported at this or nearby localities by Tanner and Tobisch (1972, p.176). The metasomatised psammite is crossed by several irregular north-trending bodies of crudely foliated material of Type I. Also present on the shores of Loch Hourn are veins of pegmatitic white albite

and green pyroxene and cavity infillings and veinlets of quartz, albite and calcite. In the northern half of the map west of Boc Mor [NG 916 260] the psammite is patchily metasomatised in zones up to 30 m across over an area of about 1 sq km to a pale isotropic or crudely foliated rock spotted with sodic amphibole and pyroxene but composed chiefly of albite. Large idioblastic crystals of sphene are a prominent constituent in this area. There are local areas of breccia of Type III in which the interstices are filled with amphibole and fine-grained iron oxide. At locality [NG 913 257] veinlets of magnetite up to 5 cm across have been recorded. In streams [NG 940 286] and [NG 943 291] near Camus-luinie Lewisian rocks have been similarly locally albitised with the development of green amphibole. A band several hundred metres long of metasomatised Lewisian can be traced by the roadside [NG 951 292] about 1 km south of Killilan.

The field relations of the sodic rocks show that the bodies postdate the regional pegmatites (e.g. at a locality in Glen Barrisdale [NG 893 033] on Sheet 62W) and are cut by felsic porphyrites and mafic microdiorites of the microdiorite suite at Loch Quoich (see above). It is of interest that the joints followed by the sheet-like masses are similarly oriented to those occupied by the intrusions of microdiorite in the Loch Hourn area.

The schistose bodies and crudely foliated sheets which follow joints differ mainly in the percentage of mafic minerals. Both rock types have been subjected to a metamorphism which produced dimensional orientation and cataclasis in the albite and a strong lineation and schistosity in the ferromagnesian minerals, mainly sodic pyroxene. At two localities ([NG 899 071] and [NG 888 004] on Sheet 62W) the cataclastic fabric is partly overgrown by undeformed sodic pyroxene, calcite and quartz. Other metasomatic rocks seem at first sight to have been formed under more static conditions, but this is probably because shearing has been localised along fractures.

The vein material falls into two categories. The albite-pyroxene rocks are affected by cataclasis, but the quartz-albite-calcite veinlets postdate any deformation in the rocks. They were probably formed at the same time as the overgrowths on the cataclastic fabric mentioned above, and are evidence that the redistribution of material continued into a period of low strain and relatively low temperature.

Though the relative chronology with regard to the regional pegmatites and microdiorites is firmly established, genetic relationships to igneous rocks remain conjectural. The geochemistry of the Loch Hourn rocks suggests that Na and Al have been added and K, Ca, Fe and Mg removed during metasomatism (Tanner and Tobisch, 1972. p.173). These authors conclude that the sodic rocks are possibly genetically related to a saturated syenitic magma, though no such parent body is exposed at the present level of erosion.

SEVEN

# Faults and mineralisation

## FAULTS

Four broad groups of faults can be recognised, these being the WSW-trending Strathconon fault complex, and three groups trending respectively north-west, east–west and approximately north–south. The first two groups are characterised by dominantly strike-slip movement. Throughout the area there are numerous examples of small crushes and faults of varying orientation and with only small displacements.

The WSW-trending Strathconon fault complex is up to 1.5 m wide. On Sheet 72W the net sinistral movement, as determined from the displacement of the Ratagain microdiorites and the Lower Devonian acid porphyrite and felsite dykes, is about 6 km, the movement having been accomplished before the intrusion of the camptonites of Permo-Carboniferous age (cf. Ramsay, 1955). A south-eastward downthrow was deduced by Simony (1963) from a comparison of the major fold structures on either side of the fault system. Supporting evidence for a net sinistral movement on the fault complex is given by a consideration of displacements of the Moine and Lewisian rocks on Sheet 71E as well as in the present area.

Within the fault complex are soft crush rocks and hard cataclasites. The former are topographically expressed as slacks and gullies such as those which are a prominent feature of the hillside south of Shiel Bridge [NG 935 187]. Although many of the belts of soft crush rock follow the general WSW trend of the complex, others are oriented north–south or more randomly. The faults with soft crush rock cut hard cataclasite and breccia formed at an earlier stage of fault movement; a large mass of such cataclasite occurs east of Bealachasan [NG 896 173], south-east of the principal displacement zone, and WSW-trending bands occur elsewhere. Psammitic rocks within the area subject to cataclasis show incipient recrystallisation of quartz, growth of sericite on grain boundaries and bending of plagioclase twinning.

Two groups of faults, one trending east–west and the other NW–SE, have been mapped in the area north-west of the Strathconon Fault. Erosion of broken rock along the faults has given rise to hollows which commonly appear as prominent features on air photographs. Exceptionally deep erosion along an east–west fault has given rise to the major valley of the River Glennan. In spite of the size of the valley the fault appears to be a relatively minor structure and the width of shattered rock appears to be less than 50 m. Exposures of the Glennan fault in a minor stream above Camus-luinie [NG 940 281] show brecciated psammite veined with hematite-stained carbonate and later white carbonate. The presence of hematite and carbonate is typical of both the east–west and NW–SE groups of faults. The fairly straight outcrops of the faults in spite of considerable topographic variation show that they are steeply ( > 50°) inclined,

a conclusion supported by a number of measurements of exposed fault planes. The relative amounts of vertical and horizontal movement are difficult to assess. However the amount of displacement of geological boundaries makes it unlikely that the gross displacement on any of the faults exceeds 500 m and in most cases it is probably less than 100 m.

South-east of the Strathconon fault system there are two north-west-trending faults on which significant dextral slip can be inferred. In the south-west, the Kinlochhourn Fault can be traced from Loch Quoich (Sheet 62W) to the Bealach Aoidhdoilean and perhaps as far as Beinn nan Coarach [NG 872 122] on Sheet 71E. The trace of the fault for most of its length north-west of Kinlochhourn is concealed by drift and alluvium, but elsewhere it forms a well-defined slack or feature in which soft crush rock has been observed. In contrast to the individual faults of the Strathconon fault complex the line of breakage is remarkably straight, the only known exception being a small fault displacement at a locality [NG 965 062] 2 km east of Kinlochhourn. The dextral displacement along the Kinlochhourn Fault is approximately 1 km. The second dextral fault, with a displacement of about 600 m, extends from the Allt na Lapaich [010 150] to the southern slopes of Sgurr a Bhealaich [NH 033 135] where it is interrupted by a later cross-fault, but it can be traced south-eastwards to the eastern limit of Sheet 72W. At a locality about 1800 m north of Creag a'Mhaim [NH 087 077], just outside the area, it displaces an ENE-trending sinistral fault. Faults in Gleann Lichd and Gleann Choinneachain [NH 99 22] may also have a dextral component.

A north-west-trending fault crosses the southern peaks of the Five Sisters of Kintail. Though vertical in orientation for much of its length, its south-easterly continuation into Glen Shiel shows a low northward dip. There is an apparent sinistral displacement of the Sgurr Beag Slide by this fault.

The north-west- and north-east-striking faults and associated joints apparently controlled the intrusion of the Lower Old Red Sandstone lamprophyre and felsite dykes. These were intruded parallel to, and in some cases along both dextral and sinistral faults. Examples can be seen in the Glen Lichd fault 500 m south-east of Glenlichd House [NH 010 168], and in the Kinlochhourn Fault where it is exposed in the Allt an Tomain Odhair [NG 897 109]. The north-west structures clearly predate much of the movement on the Strathconon fault complex since the swarm of felsite dykes is sinistrally displaced.

North or north-east-trending faults with a vertical or easterly dip occur widely in the southern part of the Kintail district, but their displacement of stratigraphical boundaries is usually negligible and they are not shown on the 1:50 000 published map. Some of these faults are followed by microdiorite dykes which have been sheared by subsequent movements. It is probable that such faults were initiated at a stage immediately following the final Caledonian metamorphic event.

The joint pattern in the area has not been examined in detail, but a WNW-trending joint system with steep or vertical dips is prominent from the south side of Kinlochhourn to the south slopes of Ben Attow, parallel to the lamprophyre dykes and dextral faults.

## MINERALISATION

Veins containing pyrite, chalcopyrite, galena, sphalerite and minor amounts of hessite and electrum have been recorded associated with the Strathconon fault complex south-west of Loch Duich. Gold is reported to occur within the electrum and silver in the galena (Alderton, 1986, 1988). The occurrence of calcite in faults is common, and at one locality [NG 984 117] there is a 4.5 m of silicified breccia. Dolomite occurs in the soft crush rock of the Strathconon fault complex. Molybdenite and fluorspar are disseminated in the quartz monzonite of the eastern part of the Ratagain complex.

A trial pit for gold and copper located near the shore of Loch Duich [NG 895 243] has been described by Peach et al. (1910). The pit was sunk into pyrite- and pyrrhotite-rich gneissose bands within the Eastern Lewisian. Analyses of selected specimens collected by the Geological Survey at the time the pit was sunk yielded gold values slightly higher than 1 dwt Au per long ton (approx 1.5 ppm). No further work appears to have been carried out since the preliminary examination in 1905.

EIGHT

# Pleistocene and Recent

## MORPHOLOGY

Although the ground in the Kintail district is considerably dissected, traces remain of erosion surfaces comparable to those of other parts of the Northern Highlands (cf. Godard, 1965). Thus the main east–west ridge on the south side of Glen Shiel shows an accordance of summit levels about 910 m above OD, and a broader area at this height forms the summit plateau of Ben Attow. Remnants of a lower surface between 460 and 610 m occur in the west, forming, for instance, the gently undulating ground of Druim na Firean [NG 905 125] and the country between Glen Elchaig and Loch Duich. There are six 'breached watersheds', Glen Elchaig to Loch Monar, Glen Elchaig to Glen Cannich, Glen Lichd to Glen Affric, Glen Shiel to Glen Moriston, Glen Quoich to Glen Loyne, and Loch Hourn to Loch Quoich. In the middle two the former 'preglacial' watershed probably lay some 3 to 4 km west of the present divide, as shown by the angles of the tributary streams to the main valleys. The main effects of glacial sculpturing on the 'preglacial' topography was probably the enlargement and deepening of the principal valleys and the modification of the ridges by corrie formation on the north and east flanks (Plate 4).

Landforms of glacial erosion are well developed in the valleys leading from the principal watershed to the sea-lochs of the west coast. In the valley-long profiles the roughly horizontal elements bounded by steeper sections are caused by rock barriers or 'riegels', best seen in upper Glen Lichd and in Glen Shiel. Of the smaller scale features, glacial grooving is well seen at several localities, for instance on the shores of Loch Hourn and at the head of Glen Lichd (Figure 19). Striae are very poorly preserved on exposed Lewisian rocks but are generally well preserved on coarse pelite, which in places retains the deeper impressions even where weathered. On psammite preservation is more variable as this rock type is more readily frost shattered than pelite. Most of the striae shown on the north-west part of the 1:50 000 Drift map were noted on the glacially smoothed surfaces of quartz veins.

## GLACIAL DEPOSITS

The characteristic glacial deposit is morainic drift, a loose unsorted stony material including a proportion of stiff boulder clay and of bedded sand and gravel (Figure 19). It is distributed as mounds or as dissected sheets in the valleys, and commonly grades upslope into hillwash. West of Cluanie Inn [NH 077 116] and in Coire Domhain [NG 987 156] the drift shows a lineation in the direction of ice movement. In the north part of the map area elongated drumlins and crag and tail features are well displayed east of Beinn Mheadhoin [NG 918 288].

Mappable areas of meltwater deposits are uncommon, the largest being in the form of peat-covered terraces in Glen Ling [NG 95 33]. A low gravel terrace is seen on both sides of Glen Shiel, upstream of Shiel Bridge. On the hillside south-west of Camus-luinie [NG 946 283] two apparently horizontal terraces cut in drift and 10 to 15 m wide extend into the large glacial drainage occupied by the River Glennan (Figure 19). These terraces seem to be the margin of a small lake formerly impounded by the glacier in Glen Elchaig. Farther east in Glen Elchaig terraces on the north side of the valley descend eastwards; they do not seem to be related to ice-front positions as there is no evidence for a glacial lake which would have overflowed across the watershed to the north-east.

The results of mass movement, including periglacial landforms and deposits formed chiefly in the late-glacial period, can be seen on many of the higher hills. Examples of solifluction terraces occur on the high ground around Glen Quoich. Landslides and rock-falls are more common on south- and east-facing slopes, for instance those on the ridge north of Glen Shiel, on the hill slopes north of the head of Loch Duich and on the south face of Ben Attow (Plate 3). In these three examples there is no landslip toe and the solid geology can be mapped through the slips with little evidence for major displacement. Many of the slips probably originated towards the end of late-glacial times and were caused by a combination of factors such as favourable orientation of joints, a high water table and relief of stress as the ice retreated from overdeepened valleys.

Deposits and landforms other than those associated with the Pleistocene ice include small stretches of postglacial (Flandrian) raised beach at 3 to 4 m above high-tide level in Loch Hourn and Loch Duich. At the head of Loch Duich [NG 93 19] a rock cliff with its base a little above high-tide level might be correlated with the Main Late-glacial Shoreline recognised by Sissons (1976) in western and south-east Scotland. Spreads of blanket and basin peat occur at low levels in the valleys and are locally present up to about 660 m above OD (Figure 19). Though small areas of alluvium can be found by most streams, extensive deposits are confined to major river valleys such as Glen Elchaig and Glen Shiel.

## DEEP DECOMPOSITION

Deep decomposition has affected the more basic rocks of the Ratagain Plutonic Complex (Godard, 1965, p.339) to depths of between 2 and 5 m, outwith the probable limits of the Loch Lomond Readvance ice. Decomposition also occurs in Lewisian calcareous rocks in Eilanriach Forest, Glen Beag on the adjoining Kyle of Lochalsh (71E) Sheet, also outside the Loch Lomond Readvance limit. The decomposition is probably partly pre-Pleistocene (Godard, 1965) and partly more recent, since clasts of Ratagain igneous rocks in glacial

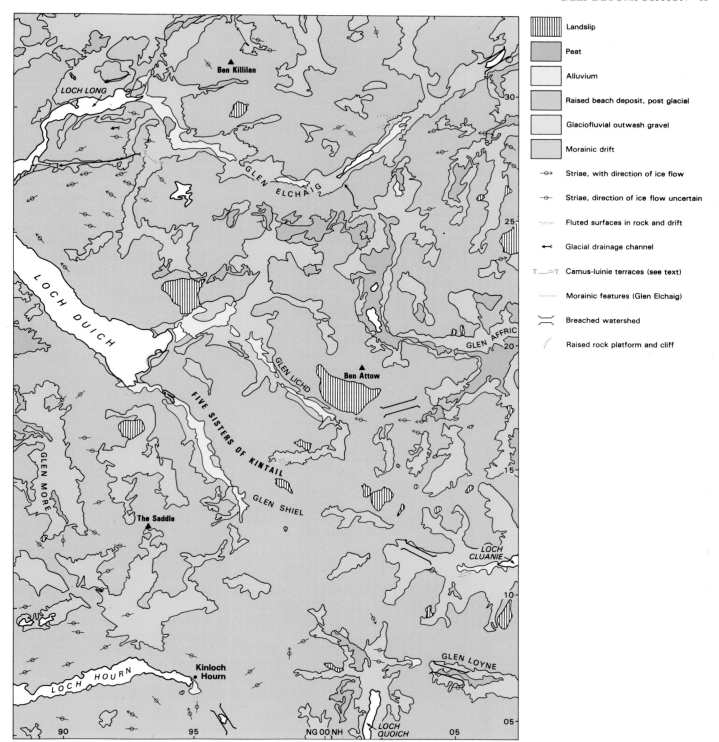

**Figure 19**   Generalised distribution of glacial deposits.

**Plate 3** Landslip features on southern slope of Ben Attow.

drift are frequently reduced to a friable state by weathering. In one section [NG 898 189] 1.5 m of gravel with decomposed ultramafic and syenite clasts overlies 1 m of decomposed 'head' and 2.5 m of decomposed ultramafic bedrock.

## GLACIAL AND LATE-GLACIAL HISTORY

In the west of the district many of the landforms and deposits, particularly those on high ground, almost certainly date from the maximum of the Late Devensian glaciation some 18 000 BP (radiocarbon-years ago) to a few thousand years later. In the east of the Sheet, however, many of the valleys were probably reoccupied by glaciers during the period of the Loch Lomond Advance, or Readvance, (LLR) between 11 000 and 10 000 BP (Peacock, 1970, 1975; Sissons, 1983, fig 14.4). On the adjoining Glen Affric (72E) Sheet the maximum extent of the eastward-flowing LLR glaciers is defined by well-marked terminal moraines (Peacock, 1970; Sissons, 1977) but in the Kintail district, the

**Plate 4**   Well-developed corries on the northern face of Ben Attow.

limits of the generally westward-flowing glaciers are conjectural for the most part, and may not correspond with the limits of hummocky moraines (see below).

### Late Devensian glaciation

At the maximum of the Late Devensian glaciation ice flowed generally from east to west across the area. The ice shed at this time is not clear, but may have been near the east margin of the sheet. It was almost certainly west of the Cluanie Granodiorite (which is exposed on both sides of Loch Cluanie a few kilometres east of the sheet margin) as no erratics of this rock type have been found west if its outcrop). Many of the highest mountains show traces of ice action almost to their summits in the form of erratics and more or less frost-shattered or weathered whaleback surfaces. Transported boulders of the coarse migmatitic pelite from east of the Sgurr Beag Slide are found near the summit of Sgurr Sgiath Airigh (881 m) [NG 926 052] south of Loch Hourn.

It is likely that many of the striations shown on the west side of the map relate to ice flow after the Late Devensian maximum but before the LLR. In the north part of the map area ice flowed northwards and westwards across the moun-tains north of Glen Elchaig, including Ben Killilan [NG 970 316]. On the high rolling country between Glen Elchaig and Loch Duich there was a generally westerly movement as shown, for instance, by striking crag-and-tail featuring east of Beinn a' Mheadhoin [NG 918 288]. South of Loch Duich ice moved westwards across the high ground west of Glen Shiel (Peach et al., 1910), this westerly flow being augmented by a northward flow across Druin na Firean [NG 905 125] from Loch Hourn into the upper Glenmore. Ice which flowed westwards across the Dubh Lochain area [NG 890 095] could, in the present state of knowledge, be of Loch Lomond Readvance age.

### Loch Lomond Readvance

The valley glaciation in the eastern half of this district is thought to have taken place during the Loch Lomond Readvance because there is no evidence for a corrie glaciation later than the last valley glaciation in an area contiguous with that in which a widespread event of this age is inferred (Peacock, 1970, 1975). Moreover, no late-glacial beaches are present in the valleys occupied by Loch Hourn, Loch Duich and Loch Long (possibly having been removed by the re-advance) and glaciofluvial terraces extend to and possibly below the level of the postglacial beach. The last two relationships are those of a former glacier terminus in Loch Carron, interpreted as being of LLR age (McCann, 1966).

Though much of the ice flow (as determined from striae, roches moutonnées, and the carry of erratics) was related to the local topography, there is evidence from lineated drift and plucked surfaces that in Glen Shiel the iceshed lay about (1.5 km) east of the present-day watershed (Peacock, 1975, fig. 1). Similarly, the ice occupying the head of Glen Affric discharged westwards across the col into Glen Lichd, as well as eastwards down the valley. Boulders of the coarse migmatitic pelites east of the Sgurr Beag Slide are to be found west of their outcrop in Glen Lichd. In the north the iceshed in Glen Cannich on the adjoining Glen Affric (72E) sheet was at the entrance of Glen na Coilich (NH 100 290), about 4 km east of the present-day watershed.

As mentioned above, the limits of the LLR glaciers are not accurately known in the Kintail district though it is possible in some cases to suggest maximum positions. Glaciofluvial terraces descend gently from north-east to south-west along Loch Long to the level of the postglacial beach at Ardelve [NG 873 267] and Nostie [NG 857 269], and the gravel islands Glas Eilean [NG 845 253] and Eilean Tioran [NG 875 260] on the Kyle of Lochalsh (71E) sheet may mark the sites of end moraines. Within this possibly maximum position for the LLR, minimum limits may be given by hummocky moraines near Sallachy [NG 915 305] near the head of Loch Long and by a glaciofluvial terrace on the south side of Glen Shiel at Shiel Bridge [NG 935 188]. The former position would be in keeping with an ice-marginal lake at Camus-luinie in Glen Elchaig (see above).

West of the Saddle [NG 936 131] the ice of the Loch Lomond Readvance stage may have been less extensive than to the east. In the valley of the Glenmore River the limit of the Readvance may have been at Suardalan [NG 883 173] which is the western limit of fresh moundy moraine. In Glen Beag local glaciers from the Beinn Sgritheall group terminated near Balvraid [NG 847 166].

# REFERENCES

AFTALION, M, VAN BREEMAN, O, and BOWES, D R. 1984. Age constraints on basement of the Midland Valley of Scotland. *Transactions of the Royal Society of Edinburgh*, Vol. 75, 53–64.

ALDERMAN, A R. 1936. Eclogites in the neighbourhood of Glenelg, Inverness-shire. *Quarterly Journal of the Geological Society of London*, Vol. 92, 488–528.

ALDERTON, D H M. 1986. Hessite and electrum from the Ratagain intrusion, north-west Scotland. *Mineralogical Magazine*, Vol. 50, 179.

— 1988. Ag-Au-Te mineralisation in the Ratagain complex, northwest Scotland. *Transactions of the Institute of Mining and Metallurgy (Section B: Applied earth sciences)*, Vol. 97, 171–180.

BAILEY, E B, and TILLEY, C E. 1952. Rocks claimed as conglomerate at the Moinian–Lewisian junction. *International Geological Congress Report*, Part 13, 272.

BAIRD, A W. 1982. The Sgurr Beag Slide within Moine rocks at Loch Eilt, Inverness-shire. *Journal of the Geological Society of London*, Vol. 139, 647–653.

BARBER, A J. 1965. The history of the Moine Thrust zone, Lochcarron and Lochalsh, Scotland. *Proceedings of the Geologists Association*, Vol. 176, 215–242.

— 1968. The geology of the country round Dornie, Wester Ross. Unpublished PhD thesis, University of London.

— BEACH, A, PARK, R G, TARNEY, J, and STEWART, A D. 1978. The Lewisian and Torridonian rocks of North West Scotland. *Proceedings of the Geologists' Association*, Guide No. 21.

— and MAY, F. 1976. The history of the Western Lewisian in the Glenelg Inlier, Lochalsh, Northern Highlands. *Scottish Journal of Geology*, Vol. 12, 35–50.

BARR, D. 1985. Migmatites in the Moines. 225–264 in *Migmatites*. ASHWORTH, J R (editor). (Glasgow: Blackie and Son.)

BAXTER, A N, and MITCHELL, J G. 1984. Camptonite-monchiquite dyke swarms of Northern Scotland: age relationships and their significance. *Scottish Journal of Geology*, Vol. 20, 297–308.

BROOK, M quoted in BROWN, G C, FRANCIS, E H, KENNAN, P, and STILLMAN, C J. (1985). Caledonian igneous rocks of Britain and Ireland. 1–15 *in* The nature and timing of orogenic activity in the Caledonian rocks of the British Isles. HARRIS, A L (editor). *Memoir of the Geological Society of London*, No. 9, 1–15.

BROWN, R L, DALZIEL, I W D, and JOHNSON, M R W. 1970. A review of the structure and stratigraphy of the Moinian of Ardgour, Moidart and Sunart-Argyll and Inverness-shire. *Scottish Journal of Geology*, Vol. 6, 309–335.

CLIFFORD, T N. 1957. The stratigraphy and structure of part of the Kintail district of southern Ross-shire: its relation to the Northern Highlands. *Quarterly Journal of the Geological Society of London*, Vol. 113, 57–92.

CLOUGH, C T. 1901. *Memoirs of the Geological Survey, Summary of Progress for 1900.* 8–9.

COBBOLD, P R, and QUINQUIS, H. 1980. Development of sheath folds in shear regimes. *Journal of Structural Geology*, Vol. 2, 119–126.

DEARNLEY, R. 1967. Metamorphism of minor intrusions associated with the Newer Granites of the Western Highlands of Scotland. *Scottish Journal of Geology*, Vol. 3, 449–457.

DHONAU, T J. 1960. The geology of the Five Sisters of Kintail. Unpublished PhD thesis, University of London.

— 1964. A possible extension of the Ratagain Igneous Complex, Wester Ross and Inverness-shire. *Geological Magazine*, Vol. 101, 37–39.

FLEUTY, M J. 1964. The description of folds. *Proceedings of the Geologists' Association*, Vol. 75, 461–492.

— 1974. The Beinn Bhreac fold, Southern Ross-shire. *Scottish Journal of Geology*, Vol. 10, 229–235.

GEOLOGICAL SURVEY OF GREAT BRITAIN. *Summary of progress for 1962, 1963 and 1964.* (London: Her Majesty's Stationery Office.)

GODARD, A. 1965. *Recherches de geomorphologie en Ecosse du Nord-Ouest.* (Paris: University of Strasburg.)

GUPPY, E M, and THOMAS, H H. 1931. Chemical analyses of igneous rocks, metamorphic rocks and minerals. *Memoir of the Geological Survey of the UK.*

HALLIDAY, A N, AFTALION, M, PARSONS, I, DICKIN, A P, and JOHNSON, M R W. 1987. Syn-orogenic alkaline magmatism and its relationship to the Moine Thrust Zone and the thermal state of the lithosphere in NW Scotland. *Journal of the Geological Society of London*, Vol. 144, 611–617.

— DICKIN, A P, FALLICK, A E, STEPHENS, W E, HUTTON, D H W, YARDLEY, B W D, and HARMON, R S. 1984. Open mantle and crust systems during ascent and emplacement of Late Caledonian alkali-rich magmas: a detailed multidisciplinary study of the Ratagain complex, NW Scotland. *Proceedings of the Symposium on Open Magmatic Systems, Taos, New Mexico*, 175–176.

— and STEPHENS, W E. 1984. Crustal controls on the genesis of the 400 Ma old Caledonian granites. *Physics of the Earth and Planetary Interiors*, Vol. 35, 89–104.

HASELOCK, P J, WINCHESTER, J A, and WHITTLES, K H. 1982. The stratigraphy and structure of the southern Monadhliath Mountains between Loch Killin and upper Glen Roy. *Scottish Journal of Geology*, Vol. 18, 275–290.

HIGGINS, M W. 1971. Cataclastic rocks. *Professional Paper of the US Geological Survey*, No. 687.

HOLDSWORTH, R E, HARRIS, A L, and ROBERTS, A M. 1987. The stratigraphy, structure and regional significance of the Moine Rocks of Mull, Argyllshire, W. Scotland. *Geological Journal*, Vol. 22, 83–107.

HOLMES, G, and JARVIS, J J. 1985. Large scale toppling within a sackung type deformation at Ben Attow, Scotland. *Quarterly Journal of Engineering Geology*, Vol. 18, 287–289.

HUTTON, D H W. 1988. Granite emplacement mechanisms and tectonic controls: inferences from deformation studies. *Transactions of the Royal Society of Edinburgh*, Vol. 79, 245–255.

— STEPHENS, W E, YARDLEY, B, McERLEAN, M, and HALLIDAY, A N. 1990. The Ratagain Plutonic Complex. *Technical Report, British Geological Survey*, No. WA/90/79.

JOHNSTONE, G S, and MYKURA, W. 1989. *British regional geology: the Northern Highlands of Scotland* (4th edition). (London: HMSO for British Geological Survey.)

— SMITH, D I, and HARRIS, A L. 1969. The Moinian assemblages of Scotland. 159–180 in North Atlantic — geology and continental drift. KAY, M (editor). *Memoir of the American Association of Petroleum Geologists*, Vol. 12, 159–180.

LAMBERT, R ST J, WINCHESTER, J A, and HOLLAND, J G. 1979. Time, space and intensity relationships of the Precambrian and lower Palaezoic metamorphism of the Scottish highlands. 363–366 in The Caledonides of the British Isles — reviewed. HARRIS, A L, LEAKE, B E, and HOLLAND, C H (editors). *Special Publication of the Geological Society of London*, No. 8.

LANGFORD, R L. 1980. Deformation in the Moine south-east of Glen Carron Highland Region, Scotland. Unpublished PhD thesis, Kingston Polytechnic, Surrey.

McCANN, S B. 1966. The limits of the Late-glacial Highland, or Loch Lomond Readvance along the West Highland seaboard from Oban to Mallaig. *Scottish Journal of Geology*, Vol. 2, 84–95.

McGREGOR, A G. 1948. Resemblances between Moine and 'Sub-Moine' metamorphic sediments in the Western Highlands of Scotland. *Geological Magazine*, Vol. 85, 265–275.

McLEISH, A J. 1971. Strain analysis of deformed pipe rock in the Moine Thrust zone, northwest Scotland. *Tectonophysics*, Vol. 12, 469–503.

MERCY, E L P, and O'HARA, M J. 1968. Nepheline normative eclogite from Loch Duich, Ross-shire. *Scottish Journal of Geology*, Vol. 4, 1–9.

MOORHOUSE, S J, and MOORHOUSE, V E. 1983. The geology and geochemistry of the Strathy complex of North-East Sutherland, Scotland. *Mineralogical Magazine*, Vol. 47, 123–137.

NICHOLLS, G D. 1951a. The Glenelg-Ratagain Igneous Complex. *Quarterly Journal of the Geological Society of London*, Vol. 106 (for 1950), 309–344.

— 1951b. An unusual pyroxene-rich xenolith in the diorite of the Glenelg-Ratagain Igneous Complex. *Geological Magazine*, Vol. 88, 284–295.

PEACH, B N, HORNE, J, GUNN, W, CLOUGH, C T, HINXMAN, L, and TEALL, J J H. 1907. The geological structure of the North West Highlands of Scotland. *Memoir of the Geological Survey of Scotland*.

— — HINXMAN, L W, CRAMPTON, C B, ANDERSON, E M, and CARRUTHERS, R G. 1913. The geology of Central Ross-shire. *Memoir of the Geological Survey of Scotland*, Sheet 82.

— — WOODWARD, H B, CLOUGH, C T, HARKER, A, and WEDD, C B. 1910. The geology of Glenelg, Lochalsh and South East part of Skye. *Memoir of the Geological Survey of Scotland*, Sheet 71.

PEACOCK, J D. 1967. West Highland morainic features aligned in the direction of ice flow. *Scottish Journal of Geology*, Vol. 3, 370–371.

— 1970. Some aspects of the glacial geology of West Inverness-shire. *Bulletin of the Geological Survey of Great Britain*, No. 33, 43–56.

— 1975. Palaeoclimatic significance of ice-movement directions of Loch Lomond Readvance glaciers in Glen Moriston and Glen Affric areas, northern Scotland. *Bulletin of the Geological Survey of Great Britain*, No. 49, 39–42.

— 1981. Report and excursion guide — Lewis and Harris. *Quaternary Newsletter*, No. 35, 45–54.

— and BERRIDGE, N. 1971. *In discussion of* The Sgurr Beag Slide — a major tectonic break within the Moinian of the Western Highlands of Scotland. TANNER, P W G. *Proceedings of the Geological Society of London*, No. 1664, 260.

POWELL, D. 1974. Stratigraphy and structure of the Western Moine and the problem of Moine orogenesis. *Quarterly Journal of the Geological Society of London*, Vol. 130, 573–593.

— BAIRD, A W, CHARNLEY, N R, and JORDAN, P J. 1981. The metamorphic environment of the Sgurr Beag slide; a major crustal displacement zone in Proterozoic, Moine rocks of Scotland. *Quarterly Journal of the Geological Society of London*, Vol. 138, 661–673.

RAMSAY, J G. 1955. A camptonitic dyke suite at Monar, Ross-shire and Inverness-shire. *Geological Magazine*, Vol. 92, 297–308.

— 1957. Moine–Lewisian relations at Glenelg, Inverness-shire. *Quarterly Journal of the Geological Society of London*, Vol. 113, 487–523.

— 1960. The deformation of early linear structures in areas of repeated folding. *Journal of Geology*, Vol. 68, 75–93.

— 1963. Structure and metamorphism of the Moine and Lewisian Rocks of the northwest Caledonides. 143–175 in *The British Caledonides*. JOHNSON, M R W, and STEWART, F H (editors). (Edinburgh: Oliver and Boyd.)

— 1967. *Folding and fracturing of rocks.* (New York: McGraw-Hill.)

— and SPRING, J S. 1962. Moine stratigraphy in the Western Highlands of Scotland. *Proceeding of the Geologists' Association*, Vol. 73, 295–326.

RAST, N. 1958. Tectonics of the Schiehallion complex. *Quarterly Journal of the Geological Society of London*, Vol. 114, 25–46.

RATHBONE, P A, and HARRIS, A L. 1979. Basement-cover relationships at Lewisian inliers in the Moine rocks. 101–108 in The Caledonides of the British Isles — reviewed. HARRIS, A L, HOLLAND, C H, and LEAKE, B E (editors). *Special Publications of the Geological Society of London*, No. 8.

READ, H H, and DOUBLE, I S. 1935. On the occurrence of chondrodite in the Glenelg limestone of Inverness-shire. *Mineralogical Magazine*, Vol. 24, 84–89.

— PHEMISTER, J, and ROSS, G. 1926. The geology of Strath Oykell and Lower Loch Shin. *Memoir of the Geological Survey of Scotland*, Sheet 102.

RICHEY, J E, and KENNEDY, W Q. 1939. The Moine and Sub-Moine Series of Morar, Inverness-shire. *Bulletin of the Geological Survey of Great Britain*, No. 2, 26–45.

ROBERTS, A M, and HARRIS, A L. 1983. The Quoich Line — a limit of early Palaeozoic crustal reworking in the Moine of the Northern Highlands of Scotland. *Quarterly Journal of the Geological Society of London*, Vol. 140, 883–892.

— and SMITH, D I, and HARRIS, A L. 1984. The structural setting and tectonic significance of the Glen Dessary syenite, Inverness-shire. *Quarterly Journal of the Geological Society of London*, Vol. 141, 1033–1042.

ROCK, N M S. 1983. The Permo-Carboniferous camptonite–monchiquite dyke-suite of the Scottish Highlands and Islands; distribution, field and petrological aspects. *Report of the Institute of Geological Sciences*, No. 82/14.

— 1985. A compilation of analytical data for metamorphic limestones from the Scottish Highlands & Islands, with lists of BGS registered samples, and comments on the reproducibility and accuracy of limestones analyses by different analytical techniques. *Mineralogical and Petrological Report British Geological Survey*, No. 85/5.

— 1986. The geochemistry of Lewisian marbles. 109–126 *in* Evolution of the Lewisian and comparable Precambrian high grade terrains. PARK, R G, and TARNEY, J (editors). *Special Publication of the Geological Society of London*, No. 27.

— MACDONALD, R, SZUCS, T, and BOWER, J. 1986. The comparative geochemistry of some Highland pelites. (Anomalous local limestone-pelite successions within the Moine outcrop). *Scottish Journal of Geology*, Vol. 22, 179–202.

ROGERS, G, and DUNNING, G R. 1991. Geochronology of appinitic and related granitic magmatism in the Highlands of Scotland: constraints on the timing of transcurrent fault movement. *Journal of the Geological Society of London*, Vol. 148, 17–27.

SANDERS, I S. 1972. The petrology of eclogites and related rocks at Glenelg, Inverness-shire. Unpublished PhD thesis, University of Cambridge.

— VAN CALSTEREN, P W C, and HAWKESWORTH, J. 1984. A Grenville Sm-Nd age for the Glenelg eclogite in north-west Scotland. *Nature, London*, Vol. 312, 439–440.

SIMONY, P S. 1963. Geology of the Saddle area. Unpublished PhD thesis, University of London.

— 1973. Lewisian sheets within the Moines around 'The Saddle' of northwest Scotland. *Journal of the Geological Society of London*, Vol. 129, 191–204.

SISSONS, J B. 1976. *The geomorphology of the British Isles: Scotland.* (London: Methuen and Co. Ltd.)

— 1977. Former ice-dammed lakes in Glen Moriston, Inverness-shire, and their significance in upland Britain. *Transactions of the Institute of British Geographers*, Vol. 2, 224–242.

— 1983. Quaternary. 399–424 in *Geology of Scotland* (2nd edition, revised). CRAIG, G Y (editor). (Edinburgh: Scottish Academic Press.)

SMITH, D I. 1979. Caledonian minor intrusions of the N. Highlands of Scotland. 683–687 *in* The Caledonides of the British Isles — reviewed. HARRIS, A L, HOLLAND, C H, AND LEAKE, B E (editors). *Special Publications of the Geological Society of London*, No. 8.

STEPHENS, W E, and HALLIDAY, A N. 1984. Geochemical contrasts between late Caledonian granitoid plutons of northern, central and southern Scotland. *Transactions of the Royal Society of Edinburgh*, Vol. 75, 259–273.

— — HUTTON, D H W, and YARDLEY, B W. 1984. The Ratagain pluton, Kintail: an example of shoshonitic magmatism in the Scottish Caledonian. *Quarterly Journal Geological Society of London, Newsletter*, No. 13, 45.

STRECKEISEN, A. 1976. To each plutonic rock its proper name. *Earth-Science Reviews*, Vol. 12, 1–33.

SUTTON, J, and WATSON, J. 1958. Structures in the Caledonides between Loch Duich and Glenelg, North-West Highlands. *Quarterly Journal of the Geological Society of London*, Vol. 114, 231–258.

TANNER, P W G. 1965. Structural and metamorphic history of the Kinloch Hourn area, Inverness-shire, Scotland. Unpublished PhD thesis, University of London.

— 1971. The Sgurr Beag Slide, a major tectonic break within the Moinian of the Western Highlands of Scotland. *Quarterly Journal of the Geological Society of London*, Vol. 126, 435–463.

— JOHNSTONE, G S, SMITH, D I, and HARRIS, A L. 1970. Moinian stratigraphy and the problem of the central Ross-shire inliers. *Bulletin of the Geological Society of America*, Vol. 81, 299–306.

— and TOBISCH, O T. 1972. Sodic and ultra-sodic rocks of metasomatic origin from part of the Moine Nappe. *Scottish Journal of Geology*, Vol. 8, 151–178.

TEALL, J J H. 1891. On an eclogite from Loch Duich. *Mineralogical Magazine*, Vol. 9, 217–218.

THIRLWALL, M F. 1982. Systematic variation in chemistry and Nd-Sr isotopes across a Caledonian calc-alkaline volcanic arc: implications for source materials. *Earth and Planetary Science Letters*, Vol. 58, 27–50.

— 1988. Geochronology of Late Caledonian magmatism in northern Britain. *Journal of the Geological Society of London*, Vol. 145, 951–967.

TILLEY, C E. 1936. Eulysites and related rock types from Loch Duich, Ross-shire. *Mineralogical Magazine*, Vol. 24, 331–342.

TOBISCH, O T, FLEUTY, M J, MERH, S S, MUKHOPADHYAY, D, and RAMSAY, J G. 1970. Deformational and metamorphic history of Moinian and Lewisian rocks between Strathconon and Glen Affric. *Scottish Journal of Geology*, Vol. 6, 243–265.

TUCKER, M E. 1982. Precambrian dolomites: petrographic and isotopic evidence that they differ from Phanerozoic dolomites. *Geology*, Vol. 10, 7–12.

TURNELL, H B. 1985. Palaemagnetism and Rb-Sr ages of the Ratagain and Comrie intrusions. *Geophysical Journal*, Vol. 83, 363–378.

VAN BREEMEN, O, AFTALION, M, PANKHURST, R J, and RICHARDSON, S W. 1979. Age of the Loch Borralan complex, Assynt, and late movements along the Moine Thrust Zone. *Journal of the Geological Society of London*, Vol. 136, 489–496.

WILKINSON, P, SOPER, N J, and BELL, A M. 1975. Skolithus pipes as strain markers in mylonites. *Tectonophysics*, Vol. 38, 143–157.

# INDEX

**BRITISH GEOLOGICAL SURVEY**

Keyworth, Nottingham NG12 5GG
(0602) 363100

Murchison House, West Mains Road, Edinburgh EH9
3LA
031-667 1000

London Information Office, Natural History Museum
Earth Galleries, Exhibition Road, London SW7 2DE
071 589 4090

The full range of Survey publications is available
through the Sales Desks at Keyworth and at Murchison
House, Edinburgh, and in the BGS London
Information Office in the Natural History Museum
Earth Galleries. The adjacent bookshop stocks the
more popular books for sale over the counter. Most
BGS books and reports are listed in HMSO's Sectional
List 45, and can be bought from HMSO and through
HMSO agents and retailers. Maps are listed in the BGS
Map Catalogue, and can be bought from Ordnance
Survey agents as well as from BGS.

*The British Geological Survey carries out the geological survey
of Great Britain and Northern Ireland (the latter as an
agency service for the government of Northern Ireland), and
of the surrounding continental shelf, as well as its basic
research projects. It also undertakes programmes of British
technical aid in geology in developing countries as arranged
by the Overseas Development Administration.*

*The British Geological Survey is a component body of the
Natural Environment Research Council.*

HMSO publications are available from:

**HMSO Publications Centre**
(Mail, fax and telephone orders only)
PO Box 276, London SW8 5DT
Telephone orders 071-873 9090
General enquiries 071-873 0011
Queueing system in operation for both numbers
Fax orders 071-873 8200

**HMSO Bookshops**
49 High Holborn, London WC1V 6HB
(counter service only)
071-873 0011    Fax 071-873 8200
258 Broad Street, Birmingham B1 2HE
021-643 3740    Fax 021-643 6510
Southey House, 33 Wine Street, Bristol BS1 2BQ
0272-264306    Fax 0272-294515
9 Princess Street, Manchester M60 8AS
061-834 7201    Fax 061-833 0634
16 Arthur Street, Belfast BT1 4GD
0232-238451    Fax 0232-235401
71 Lothian Road, Edinburgh EH3 9AZ
031-228 4181    Fax 031-229 2734

**HMSO's Accredited Agents**
(see Yellow Pages)

*And through good booksellers*